SOIL HUSBANDRY

SOIL HUSBANDRY

A Practical Guide to the Use and Management of Soils

Tom Batey

Soil and Land Use Consultants Ltd, Aberdeen

First published 1988
© T. Batey 1988

British Library Cataloguing in Publication Data
Batey, Thomas, 1933-
  Soil Husbandry
1 Soils.   Cultivation
I. Title
631.4

ISBN: 0 9513605 0 7
 Pbk: 0 9513605 1 5

Disk conversion by A.L. Downloading Services
Phototypeset in Times New Roman
by Milton Publications, Banchory
Printed in Great Britain by Aberdeen University Press

for the Publisher:

Soil and Land Use Consultants Limited
P.O. Box 294, Aberdeen AB9 8GF

CONTENTS

CHAPTER 13 Land Restoration and Reclamation

CHAPTER 14 Physical Examination of Soils in the Field

CHAPTER 15 Good Soil Husbandry   149

APPENDIX   151

List of Tables

List of Figures

List of figures

ACKNOWLEDGEMENTS

Many people have contributed both directly and indirectly to the ideas expressed in this book; colleagues in Universities, ex-colleagues in ADAS (formerly NAAS) and particularly those in the farming community, whose penetrating questions have often presented a formidable challenge.

I would like to pay particular tribute to several individuals:
to John Green for his enthusiastic support of good soil husbandry over many years and for his encouragement in its prac tice;

to Ken Simpson for his diligent work on each draft and for many helpful suggestions for their improvement;

to Chris Mullins, Ken Killham, Eric Farr, Donald MacLeod, R J A Jones and Professor Joseph Tinsley for reading various drafts and for many helpful comments

For permission to quote data from published sources I am indebted to Dr A H Weir & Dr P B Barraclough, Rothamsted, Dr D J Greenwood F R S, Wellesbourne, Mr J Meerwold, Clerk of Stationery, MAFF HQ, Mr D J Eagle, ADAS Cambridge, Dr D B Soane, SCAE, Edinburgh, the Meteorological Office, Bracknell, the Forestry Commission, Farnham, the Liaison Officer, AGRI Hurley, The Controller, H M S O, London, Faber and Faber for the quotation from 'Human Ecology' at the begining of the Introduction, Professor J S Bibby, Director, Soil Survey of Scotland, Dr P Bullock, Director, Soil Survey of England and Wales. The photographs of thin section micrographs were provided by Dr E A FitzPatrick.

Thanks are also due to Helen Sutherland for skilfully preparing the line drawings and figures, to Ken Fuller for preparing the black and white prints, finally to Beth, my wife, not only for typing the texts, but for much helpful criticism, and to James, my elder son, for help in editing and preparing the index.

INTRODUCTION

"The soil must be man's most treasured possession: so he who tends the soil wisely and with care is assuredly the foremost among men".
— *Sir George Stapleton.*

Farmers and those who work on the land come face to face with soil problems and it is they who have to make decisions on the spot, without laboratory or research facilities at hand, and with experience as the only guide. This book is aimed at them and at anyone with an interest in using and caring for the soil.

This is not strictly a textbook but more equivalent to a guide book. A framework and background to the care of soils is presented in a way that combines the principles of science with the practice and art of cultivation, used in its widest sense. Anyone requiring a more detailed account of the principles of soil science is referred to introductory and advanced texts listed in Appendix 1.

The text has been divided into two sections. The first provides some of the scientific background to good soil husbandry: the requirements of crops, the role of soil structure and soil organic matter, the importance of water in soils. The second section gives examples of soil husbandry in practice with a range of real-life problems from both arable and grassland, concentrating on practical aspects. Much emphasis is placed on the value and techniques of examination and assessment of soils directly in the field; this is frequently not included or inadequately covered in standard textbooks. *"I don't know what to look for"* is an all too common plea made initially by even the keenest observer of soils; their complexity and variation can present a bewildering picture. How to examine soils and what to look for in the field is therefore one of the key sections of the book (Chapter 14).

While many photographs and sketches are included, a book can only be a substitute for direct examination in the field. The examples given and the ideas and concepts expressed are provided to guide and encourage tillers of the soil to regard soil examination as a normal, routine part of their farming, not just as a one-off occasion to deal with a specific problem. The examples of soil problems have been selected from the author's experience. Obviously they cannot cover every situation but serve to illustrate the need for a careful, thorough and systematic examination of soils before making decisions on their management and use. Just as a stockman can 'eye' an animal and assess its well-being, so should a tiller of the soil be able to observe and evaluate the quality of the material he manipulates for his livelihood.

Soil is one of mankind's most important natural resources but it is not inert or constant; its properties change as it is used or, in some cases, misused. These properties, chemical, physical and biological, reflect a combination of inherent characteristics and those brought about by man's use of the land. Soil husbandry too, must be flexible and respond to meet the pressures and constraints in an ever changing environment.

The soil features of most concern in farming today are compaction, drainage, and structure. These are linked in complex ways and the origin and consequences of each will be examined from several viewpoints. However, I make no apology for repeating throughout the text the importance of these three factors because they are so fundamental to good soil husbandry.

Extensive research has been carried out on soils and countless reports published. However, much of this is written by scientists for scientists. When, for example, terminology such as 'medium subangular blocky structure' and 'friable consistence' is used this conveys little to the non-specialist. Such language may be essential for the soil scientist but can detract from the interesting and practical aspects of the subject by hindering communication, despite the significance and value of these expressions. One of the objectives of the book is to use as little jargon as possible and to present ideas and concepts in a straightforward manner without in any way sacrificing accuracy for simplicity.

The reproduction of slides and photographs does not always give a clear and adequate illustration, as extraneous detail may obscure the main point. Therefore many photographs have been converted to sketches, to clarify and highlight the detail of interest. This technique has also enabled descriptive records and field experience to be added. All sketches presented in this way are based on a field situation known to the author. The sketches, photographs and tables are numbered in sequence within each Chapter, thus Figure 14.2 is the second Figure to occur in Chapter 14. Metric units have been used throughout. A Table of units and conversions to a range of older units is included in the Appendix.

SECTION A   THE SCIENTIFIC BACKGROUND TO SOIL HUSBANDRY

Chapter 1   THE GROWTH OF PLANTS

Plants are the source, either directly or indirectly, of almost all the energy used by animals (including mankind) for food and fuel. Our dependence on plants is absolute. Therefore the objective of growing a selected plant as a field crop is to convert solar energy into energy stored as organic forms which can be subsequently used by mankind. Soil is the medium in which the plants grow, but in its natural state, rarely provides the correct conditions to enable crop plants to grow efficiently. From time immemorial mankind has tilled and manured the soil, to change or adjust its inherent properties for his own use. Soil is also the interface between the atmosphere and the earth and as such has to bear the forces of nature — as rain, wind and frost — as well as the activities of man the cultivator.

Whatever is done to the soil, whether adding lime, fertilizer or manures, whether ploughing, cultivating or draining, the primary objective has been to provide all the conditions required to establish and sustain a crop from seedbed to harvest. The principles are the same whether the land is used for farming, vegetable production, organic crops or forestry: the economic conversion of solar radiation into a desired end-product. At the same time neither the long term capability of the land nor any other part of the environment should be impaired by any of the treatments applied or techniques used to sow, grow or gather the crop.

Solar energy and plant growth

The process of photosynthesis converts two chemicals, carbon dioxide and water, into simple carbohydrates, using sunlight as the energy source. This process takes place within the leaf and other green surfaces of plants such as stems and ears of grain crops. However, only part of the radiant energy from the sun is used in this way. At best, a plant can convert only about 6% of the total incoming solar radiation into 'stored energy'. Over the year, a conversion figure of about 2% is typical for many crops. In order to operate efficiently plants require a regular and adequate supply of water, oxygen, carbon dioxide and nutrients as well as warmth and light.

Water enters the plant mainly through the roots and brings with it essential nutrients; carbon dioxide enters as a gas, almost all through holes (stomata) present on leaves and other green parts of the plant. These stomata are thus an essential pathway for the input of one of the essential ingredients; they are very small and can be seen only with a microscope but their role is crucial to the basic process of photosynthesis. When fully open their total area may be up to 2% of the surface of a leaf. Stomata open and close in response to various stimuli; light induces them to open, they close in the dark and in response to adverse conditions such as lack of water or high temperature. When open they permit carbon dioxide to enter, but simultaneously water vapour is lost by evaporation from inside the leaf (transpiration). The importance of the role of stomata is emphasised by the fact that for a crop growing vigorously in early summer a daily inflow of carbon dioxide of over 150 kg/ha is needed, the amount contained in the air above the crop to a height of over 20 metres. The amount of water lost while the stomata are open is related to the weather, with most needed in hot dry windy conditions, when up to 50 t/ha each day may be required. If this amount of water cannot be supplied, the stomata react by closing to cut down water loss and to prevent the leaf from drying up. When this occurs, carbon dioxide entry is also reduced leading to a fall in the rate of growth. Thus, for efficient growth, an adequate supply of water must be available in the soil to replace that lost by evaporation through the leaf stomata. Plants growing naturally in very adverse climates such as deserts, have special adaptations to conserve water, and stimuli for the opening and closing of stomata may even be the reverse of some of those described above. In warmer climates the amount of water lost through transpiration may be up to double the rates shown above.

One of the surprising facts of nature is that the rate of conversion of solar radiation to carbohydrate is similar for many plants grown as crops, whether grass, vegetables, wheat, barley or potatoes. In temperate climates, many crops increase their dry weight by about 200 kg/ha each day, once full ground cover has been reached in late spring and summer, provided that neither water nor nutrients are limiting growth. Only a proportion of this new material ends up as harvestable crop, typically about half; the remainder goes to form other components such as leaves, roots, stems or flowers.

Crop development   In the period between sowing or planting a crop and the appearance of a leaf above ground, the plant can only draw for sustenance upon the reserves of carbohydrate stored in the seed or tuber. Only when the shoot appears above ground can photosynthesis begin, to generate new carbohydrate. If there is a long delay, between germination and emergence either because of weather or because of over-deep sowing, then when leaves eventually appear they may be weak and prone to injury by frost or wind. However, if sown too shallow germination and emergence may be delayed by lack of water in the dry layer of soil on the surface.

Once a crop has emerged, the growth rate is related mainly to temperature, and to sunlight but is also proportional to the area of leaf above ground, i.e. more leaf, more growth. For example, when a turnip or sugar beet plant first comes through the ground the leaf may cover less than 3% of the land surface and therefore whatever the weather it can increase its mass only slowly. As the plants grow larger and the leaf area increases, the rate of growth increases until full crop cover is reached, and little or no bare soil is then visible.

When a crop emerges from the ground, leaf growth is obvious. What is not so readily seen is that at the same time as a primary shoot is pushing towards the surface of the soil, a root is growing downwards. At this early stage, root growth is often faster than shoot growth in terms of distance extended for example it is common to find the roots of wheat reaching a depth of $25-35$ cm while the top of the plant may be no more than $8-12$ cm above ground. As the plants grow larger and the leaf area increases, the rate of growth increases until a full cover of leaves is present.

The nutrition of plants   There are at least 19 chemical elements required for plant growth. Some are found in such small quantities within the plant there is doubt as to whether or not they are essential. Most are supplied from the soil and all of these are taken up in water-soluble forms. Almost every soil contains adequate amounts of many of these essential elements, except required in relatively large amounts: nitrogen, potassium, phosphorus, calcium, sulphur and magnesium (plus sodium for some crops). Some soils are deficient in other (trace) elements for example manganese, boron, copper, and iron and supplementary small amounts may be required to maintain optimum growth.

Each chemical element has one or more specific functions within the plant which cannot be taken over by another. When very deficient, symptoms may be seen, which are related to the function of the element. Details on the identification and treatment of nutrient deficiencies may be obtained from appropriate books, listed in Appendix 1. Many nutrients are applied, however, without any visual sign of their deficiency; experience and experiment have shown that crops respond to these applications by giving greater yields. The use of lime, manures, fertilizers and trace elements is thus established as an important aspect of crop production and much advice is available on the materials to use, how much, when and how to apply them. The aspect of interest here is that, apart from some of the requirements of sulphur (obtained from the air) and of course all of the carbon as carbon dioxide, almost all nutrients are obtained from the soil in a soluble form. If soil is dry, nutrient intake as well as water intake may be inadequate to meet the plant's needs and reduced growth may result.

In the early stages when plants are growing slowly, the overall nutrient uptake is also small in terms of daily requirement. However, the root system is also relatively small and the concentration of some nutrients, particularly nitrogen, phosphorus and potassium must be adequate in the soil adjacent to roots to provide sufficient nutrients at their surface so that enough can be taken in to achieve a high rate of growth. This aspect seems to be particularly important for plants which initially produce rather few and sometimes thick roots such as some vegetable and root crops for which 'starter' doses of nutrients may give a large response.

Further information on soil acidity and nitrogen gains and losses from the soil is given in Chapter 11.

Chapter 2   THE GROWTH OF ROOTS

Roots have several essential functions:

● they anchor the plant and provide stability;

● they absorb water and nutrients which then move upwards through the stem to the leaves;

● they may store energy as carbohydrate for later use by the plant, sometimes but not always in specially modified roots (e.g. bulbs, tubers).

Root growth in soils

Major roots initially begin growth from the seed or later from the base of the stem or other parts of the plant and from these, lateral roots then develop. They grow downwards under the influence of gravity and if obstructed by a stone or other barrier, may be diverted before continuing to grow down through the soil.

Roots have no intrinsic ability to 'search' for anything. To say that roots 'go in search of water' is only true in the sense that one of the their principal functions is to extract water from the soil. They do not stop growing when they are surrounded by moist soil, and may continue to grow to some depth, at times when the need for water by the leaves is very slight. For example, a wheat crop sown in autumn may send roots to a depth of 1 m or more by the following April, during a time when the soil is never dry.

To grow downwards, roots must be supplied with carbohydrate from the leaves or stems either directly or via storage organs. To use this for energy, oxygen is also required and in most plants is taken from the air surrounding the roots. The exceptions are plants which are specially adapted to grow in

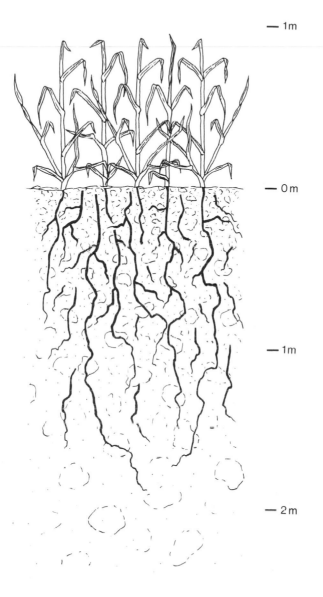

— 1m

— 0m

— 1m

— 2m

FIGURE 2.1 Deep Root Development Under Wheat.
By June, the roots of wheat may reach depths in excess of 1.8 m, provided that soil conditions are suitable.

waterlogged soil where oxygen can be transferred from above ground, through spaces within the roots.

Roots also require space of adequate size to grow through. A root tip requires the space into which it grows to be wide enough to accommodate its whole diameter or the soil must be loose enough to be pushed aside. If the spaces are too narrow or the soil too rigid, roots may penetrate only a few centimetres. In such conditions, the root may react by growing thick, stubby and contorted and may also produce extra numbers of thin roots ahead of the obstruction. Thus, if the root cannot enter a compact layer of soil, a dense interlocking web of roots may develop on the surface of the compact soil. In clayey soils which shrink and crack as they dry, roots tend to take the easiest route, that is, to follow the cracks. Thus it is is common to find roots using 'preferred' pathways in clayey soils, with few growing into the blocks of soil on either side. Despite the absence of roots in these soil blocks, the roots can extract water from them because when the soil alongside the roots in the crack dries, water can move across from the wetter soil nearby.

The depth to which roots grow is an important soil characteristic, linked to drought susceptibility. It is often a surprise to many people to realise the extent of a plant root system. Pull up a barley plant or a weed and it appears that root depth is no more than $10-20$ cm. This is highly misleading, as roots of grasses and non-perennial crops are thin, fragile and readily snapped. Root depth can be determined only by examining the soil. This can be done by digging a hole or by extracting soil with an auger. Such examination for fine roots can show roots of cereals reaching depths of 1.5 m or more. There may not be many at such depths but their presence may be important in very dry weather.

The depth to which roots grow is related to the period of time the crop has been growing, the rate of growth of the crop, the type of crop, and the properties of the soil. Under good growing conditions, roots may grow downwards as fast as $1-2$ cm per day. Typical potential root depths for a number of crops are as follows:

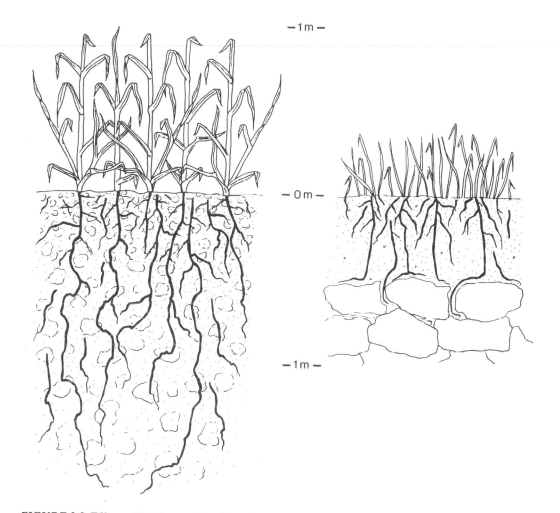

FIGURE 2.2 *Effect of Inadequate Seedbed Preparation on the Subsequent Growth of Wheat.*

The wheat had been sown in autumn after potatoes had been harvested late in wet conditions, and the seedbed prepared when patches of the land were too wet for adequate fracturing of any over-compaction caused by lifting and carting off the crop. In late spring, the growth of wheat in parts of the field was normal (left sketch), with roots growing without restriction; where compacted soil had not been effectively broken up, the crop was stunted and immature, with roots limited to a depth of about 40 cm. The surface tilth of the topsoil was similar under both normal and poor crop, but the difference in water content was striking: it was dust-dry under the poor crop and evenly moist to depth under the normal crop.

Winter wheat	1.8 − 2.0 m
Spring barley	1.2 − 1.5 m
Perennial grasses	1.2 − 2.0 m
Potatoes	0.6 − 0.8 m
Sugar beet	1.2 − 1.8 m

Reasons for restricted root growth

Restricted root growth is a common occurrence and has important implications for crop performance. Roots may be restricted in their downward growth, for a number of reasons which include:

● lack of carbohydrates as a source of energy − if the crop above ground is weak or growing slowly due to disease, pest, cold, heat or lack of nutrients then the transfer of carbohydrate to the roots may be inadequate to sustain root growth;

● a physical barrier − a dense layer can halt or greatly impede the downward growth of roots. Such a barrier may be natural, such as solid rock, cemented gravel or other physically dense material. Dense soil resulting from compaction by mechanical pressure during cultivation or harvesting may also be responsible. Where the soil beneath the topsoil is almost wholly sand, roots commonly have difficulty in growing more than a few centimetres into it.

● acidity − at pH values under about 5.0, aluminium and manganese can become so soluble in soils that they reach toxic concentrations and may kill any root present. The manganese may be transferred to the leaves and reduce their growth, but aluminium tends to remain in the root. The exact pH at which such a toxic condition occurs depends on other soil properties and on the moisture content; crops also show a range of tolerance to acid soil, discussed further in Chapter 11.

● lack of oxygen − roots require oxygen for respiration and if not present in adequate amounts, growth will be reduced or may cease. In addition, substances found in anaerobic soils may have severe adverse effects on roots. These substances may diffuse into surrounding aerated soil and thus affect roots nearby. Ethylene gas is one such substance and low concentrations can interfere adversely with plant growth.

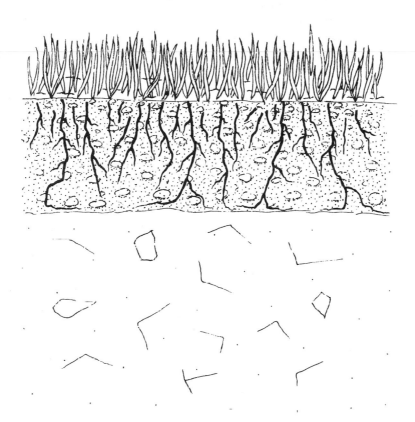

FIGURE 2.3 Roots Restricted by a Naturally Occuring Indurated Layer in NE Scotland.

Indurated layers are found in sandy and loamy soils in several areas of Northern Britain. They are so hard and dense that root entry is often impossible and crops have to grow in no more than 40 – 50 cm depth of soil. However, in the cooler and moister climate where they occur, crop yields may not be reduced except in very dry summers.

Consequences of restricted rooting

If roots cannot extend to reach their full depth, access to soil water reserves can be denied. Furthermore, because the roots are in contact with only a limited volume of soil, the available water is quickly used in dry weather and the soil becomes very dry. Nutrients present in the soil may not be absorbed as there is insufficient moisture to transfer them from soil to root. Therefore restricted rooting may lead to a reduction in crop growth either because of lack of water and/or lack of nutrients. An example of root restriction on grass growth is described in Figure 8.3. However, it must not be assumed that restricted rooting leads to crop loss in all circumstances; the critical factor to consider is the plant's need for water, which is determined by the climate. This point is discussed further in Chapter 6 and illustrated in Figures 2.3, 6.1 and 6.2.

Root development with no restriction

As an example of root development, it is worth examining in detail the results of a painstaking investigation done at Rothamsted Experimental Station, 40 km north of London. (This was reported by A.H. Weir and P.B. Barraclough in Soil Use and Management Volume 2, pages 91 − 96). Winter wheat was sown in September 1981, in a deep clayey soil. The following spring a transparent shelter was made to cover the crop, to keep out rain; the area underneath was divided into 2 plots; one was irrigated by trickle line, the other received neither rain nor irrigation from 27th March onwards. In the latter plot the wheat crop had to rely solely on water already present in the soil. One might have expected the crop growing under the cover and experiencing total drought to die off in a few weeks. However, by June roots had extended to 180 cm under both the irrigated and droughted crop though the total root length was about 10% greater in the irrigated crop (Table 1). By August, root length was less and there was little difference between the two crops. Grain yields were also similar, equivalent to 5.2 and 5.0 t/ha from the irrigated and droughted crops respectively. The water used by each crop was measured weekly. Both crops extracted water at the same rate until the middle of May by which time the droughted crop had used 100 mm of water from the soil. Water was taken from the surface layer first and then from successively deeper layers; it was not until the end of June that water was extracted from below 160 cm by the droughted crop. The amount of water extracted by the droughted crop became less with depth, particularly below 1 m. Of the total used, 159 mm was removed from 0 − 1 m and 64 mm from between 1 and 2 m depth. Almost half the root length and weight were found in the 0 − 20 cm layer and, when this became dry, the root system below was unable to meet fully the peak atmospheric demands. However, in this soil the penalty in growth and yield was small, even when the wheat crop was faced with a drought of over 4 months.

These results illustrate the considerable depth and length of roots (the total length of roots in each square metre exceeded 20 km in both crops, and water was extracted from a depth of 2 m). They also show that even though there were some roots at a great depth, their ability to meet a heavy demand for water by the crop in dry weather was limited.

Table 2.1 Length of Live Roots under Wheat, km per square metre

Depth	March, before crop	June		August	
cm	covered	Irrigated	Droughted	Irrigated	Droughted
0 − 20	3.9	12.2	9.4	7.4	7.6
20 − 100	2.9	12.4	11.2	8.3	8.9
100 − 180	−	2.6	1.8	1.7	1.5
Total length (km)	6.8	24.6	22.4	17.4	18.0

While the dominant roots of a plant are permanent structures during its life, some of the fine roots die and are replaced by new ones. Why this occurs is unclear. Live roots can usually be distinguished by their white or near-white colour and by their firm condition. Dead roots are usually brown and shrivelled or hollow. The time taken for dead roots to decompose wholly may be many months or even years depending on their original size; this delay can be helpful since the location of root remains may be an effective guide to the assessment of soil conditions or crop performance.

Chapter 3   SOIL TEXTURE

Soil texture is an expression used to describe the physical composition of the soil. Words such as clay, sand and loam have been used since ancient times to distinguish soils with different properties. Four standardised words are now used in varying combinations − sand, loam, silt and clay − to provide just over 20 different classes of texture. This must not be confused with the expression 'soil structure' which describes the way the individual particles are assembled and bound into groups, usually called aggregates.

Soil particles vary in their composition. Sands and silt sized particles are composed mainly of either quartz (silica) or other rock minerals from which the soil was formed. Clay particles, however, consist mainly of very thin platelets bound firmly into minute layered crystals, with each platelet being composed of silicon and aluminium oxides in combination with potassium, magnesium and other chemical elements.

The properties which each group of particles confer on the soil depend partly on their size and surface area, and partly on complex chemical bonding which provides clays with negatively charged external and internal surfaces. One further property of clay is important: some platelets vary in their spacing, depending on the water they contain, they shrink on drying and re-expand on wetting.

The value of soil texture assessment   Soil texture gives a guide to many soil characteristics related to its physical composition, and for this reason textural assessment is one of the most important single tests that can be done on a soil. For example each class of texture can give a guide to:

● soil water − its retention and release to plants
● soil structure − its development and stability;

- nutrient retention and availability
- activity and retention of residual soil-acting herbicides
- erodibility by wind or water
- stickiness and ease of cultivation
- drainage characteristics and suitability for moling
- cropping suitability
- soil temperature changes.

It must be appreciated that the significance of the texture of a particular layer of soil depends also on its thickness and location in a soil and on the prevailing climate. For example, a sandy soil in a dry area may be of little value for cropping without irrigation but a corresponding texture in a humid area could be very productive.

Assessment of soil texture

The sizes of the individual particles are defined precisely into three groups, with the upper limit of 'soil' set at 2 mm. Particles larger than this, grit, stones and boulders, are obviously important where present in significant numbers, and appropriate qualifying descriptions may be added.

The particles less than 2 mm are separated into 3 named groups:
sand, between 2.0 and 0.06 mm
silt, between 0.06 and 0.002 mm
clay, less than 0.002 mm.

The sizes refer to the diameter, but as many particles are not round, the expression 'equivalent spherical diameter' is used.

There are two methods available to determine soil texture. One involves analysis of the soil in a laboratory to measure the proportion of several particle sizes; the other involves an assessment of the soil as a whole by manipulating it in the hand when moist. It is the latter test of hand texturing which will be described here, as this can be done directly under field conditions.

Field method

Take about half a handful of soil , and if dry, add water to it gradually until the particles hold together to form a ball. No excess water should be present. Texture assessment is made by kneading the moist soil between fingers and thumb. It is important to work the soil down thoroughly to eliminate any small lumps (aggregates) present. The assessment is then done by estimating the contribution that the different particles, sand, silt and clay, make to the feel of the soil as a whole.

The properties of the individual fractions which determine the texture of a soil are:-

Sand — consists of grains which feel gritty, and large enough to grate against each other and may be detected individually both by touch and sight.

Silt — individual grains cannot be detected, but silt feels smooth, soapy or silky and only slightly sticky.

Clay — particles less than 0.002 mm, are characteristically sticky although some dry clays require a great deal of moistening and working between the fingers before they develop their maximum stickiness. Clay comes away fairly cleanly from the fingers, while silt is more clinging. ('Silt adheres, clay coheres.') The surface will take a polish when a finger is rubbed firmly across it.

Each class of soil texture has a characteristic tactile 'feel' to it, and is best thought of as a single entity. Special difficulties arise in soils which have a high content of organic matter or calcium carbonate: in making the texture estimate, the actual 'feel' should be recorded as for any other soil, and the contribution of the additional materials should be noted. For those unfamiliar with the technique of hand texturing, expert advice should be sought initially until experience is gained to make accurate assessments.

Soil texture class descriptions and evaluation

A brief key to the assessment of soil texture is given at the end of this Chapter, and in the Table which follows, one column describes the tactile characteristics of each class and another the important physical characteristics.

SANDY SOILS— soils dominated by sands are divided into three groups depending on the proportion of sand present, (sands, loamy sands and sandy loams) and each group is further subdivided into four according to the dominant size of the sand grains (coarse, medium, fine, very fine). (Note: the adjective medium is often omitted)

FIGURE 3.1 Assessment of Soil Texture — Field Method

The individual grains are visible in a soil texture of loamy sand which breaks apart readily under the pressure of a thumb; (below) a clay loam is highly cohesive and takes a surface polish when rubbed.

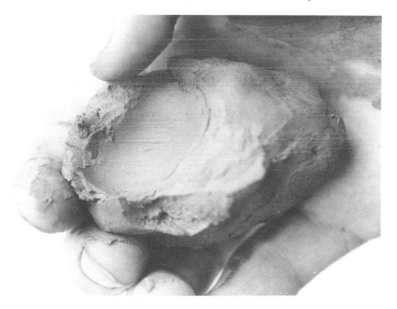

TEXTURAL DESCRIPTION	ASSOCIATED PHYSICAL PROPERTIES

SANDS

feel gritty

lack cohesion
loose when dry
not sticky at all when wet
do not stain the fingers

low retention of nutrients

COARSE SAND

particles averaging about
1 mm in size
harsh to the touch
(uncommon as a topsoil)

very droughty
fast draining
readily eroded by water

(MEDIUM) SAND

particles averaging between
0.6 − 0.2 mm
sands of the sea shore

very droughty
erodible by wind and water
root entry difficult

FINE SAND

less than 0.2 mm
dune sand

very erodible by wind and
water
root entry difficult

VERY FINE SAND

barely visible to the
naked eye
powdery, smooth
(uncommon)

LOAMY SANDS

feel gritty
slight cohesion
can be moulded into a ball
when sufficiently moist
does not stick to the
fingers

low retention of nutrients

LOAMY COARSE SAND

harsh to the touch

very droughty
fast draining
erodible by water

LOAMY (MEDIUM) SAND

as medium sand

widespread as a topsoil
low water retention
very prone to erosion by
wind, erodible by water

TEXTURAL DESCRIPTION	ASSOCIATED PHYSICAL PROPERTIES

LOAMY FINE SAND
    as fine sand

reasonable water retention
weak structure, liable to
collapse in heavy rain
crusts and caps on surface
very erodible by wind and
water

LOAMY VERY FINE SAND
    very fine powder
    (uncommon)

very weak structure, collapses
readily, easily compacted
forms hard surface cap

SANDY LOAMS

feel gritty, show a fair degree
of cohesion, can be moulded
quite readily into a ball when
just moist, yet being easily
deformed

free draining
easily worked

COARSE SANDY LOAM
    harsh and gritty very
    (uncommon as a topsoil)

very fast drainage
free working
low water retention

(MEDIUM) SANDY LOAM
    gritty
    firmly moulded

fast draining
free working
reasonable water retention
stable structure
few physical problems

FINE SANDY LOAM
    slight grittiness
    firmly moulded

fast draining
free working
good retention and release of
water, structure slightly weak
erodible by water, liable to
cap

VERY FINE SANDY LOAM
    grittiness barely detectable
    firmly moulded
    fine powdery when dry

moderately porous, weak
structure and liable to cap
surface ponding common,
excellent retention and release
of water, erodible by water,
very high value in dry areas

LOAM

a relatively even mixture of different grades of sand and of silt and clay, readily moulded into a ball, although sand present, does not feel obviously gritty. insufficient silt to impart silky feel, insufficient clay to make it sticky or take a polish.

uncommon, often associated with high organic content porous, retentive of water easy working stable structure

SILTY LOAM

smooth silky feel
sticky when wet
firmly cohesive

water retentive
adhesive and difficult to work when wet, structure usually stable but may break down if overworked, high value in dry areas less good in wet

SILT

as silty loam but smoothness, silkiness, adhesion more distinct surface will take a weak polish when rubbed firmly with finger

as silty loam but adhesion and stickiness more distinct, moderately slow draining

CLAY LOAM

sticky, bind together strongly when moist and resist deformation take a polish on surface (widespread as a topsoil)

retentive of water but release moderate, slow draining high retention of nutrients strongly developed stable structure, weathers into fine aggregates on surface high draught requirement readily smeared, shrinks on drying to form deep cracks

SANDY CLAY LOAM

as clay loam but also gritty

as clay loam but is extremely hard when dry difficult to manage under tillage, readily smeared and compressed

SILTY CLAY LOAM

as clay loam but more sticky adhesive and smooth

as clay loam but with a higher draught requirement

CLAY

very sticky, bind together
very strongly, a ball of moist
clay is very difficult to
deform by hand, takes a high
polish when moist clay
is rubbed

as clay loam but clay
characteristics more
extreme, widespread as a
subsoil below clay loam
on drying forms deep and
wide vertical cracks

SANDY CLAY

as clay but also
gritty
(uncommon)

as sandy clay loam but
clay characteristics
more extreme, very difficult
under tillage

SILTY CLAY

as clay but extremely
sticky and adhesive

as clay but very difficult
under tillage

Note: the physical properties of any of the clay textures may be improved if a few per cent of chalk is present, for example in the Chalky Boulder Clays in Eastern England; these soils drain faster and are easier to till than equivalent non-calcareous clays.

Hand Assessment of Soil Texture

Sandy soils — those with a significant amount of grittiness:-

Test the binding and cohesion:-

None .... Sands
Slight .... Loamy Sand
Readily moulded into a cohesive ball, does not
     form threads .... Sandy Loam
Moderately cohesive, sticky and plastic, forms
     threads, will take a polish on the surface .... Sandy Clay Loam
Very cohesive, very sticky, forms long threads,
     will take a high polish when rubbed .... Sandy Clay

For each of the sand groups it is also important to identify the grade of sand and the main classes should be prefixed accordingly, though for sandy clay loam and sandy clay it is less easy to identify the sand grades:

Coarse sand .... Very harsh .... 2.0 — 0.6 mm
Medium sand .... Moderately harsh, e.g.
               sea shore sand .... 0.6 — 0.2 mm
Fine sand .... Slightly gritty, e.g.
               dune sand .... 0.2 — 0.06 mm
Very fine sand.......... Smooth and powdery,
               only just visible to
               the naked eye .... 06 — 0.02 mm

Clayey soils — those which are not gritty, but are strongly cohesive, form threads and rings easily and the surface can readily take a polish when rubbed with thumb or finger:-

Moderately sticky, deforms readily when squeezed...Clay Loam
Extremely sticky, moderately smooth. difficult
     to deform .... Silty Clay Loam
Extremely cohesive, forms long threads and rings,
     high degree of polish when rubbed .... Clay
Extremely cohesive, high polish, also smooth
     and silky .... Silty Clay

Silty soils — those dominated by a smooth, soapy slipperiness or silkiness, moderately cohesive. Silt adheres readily and fingers beome very dirty; clay coheres, i.e. sticks to itself and fingers remain relatively clean.

Smoothness and silkiness dominant .... Silty Loam

Loam — where none of the above fractions, sand, silt or clay impart a dominant feel; moderately smooth and can be rolled into short threads; no polish can be obtained when rubbed .... Loam

Chapter 4   SOIL STRUCTURE

Observations on soil structure must have been made in one way or another ever since man began to disturb the soil in preparation for planting seeds. The expression 'structure' describes the size, shape and stability of the units into which the individual particles in a soil are combined and to the spaces between and within them. The relevance of structure to good soil husbandry lies in the key role played by the spaces, as it is here that the action takes place — drainage of water, aeration and the passage of roots. The spaces in the soil (pores) are also where countless organisms live ranging in size from microscopic bacteria to earthworms and beetles. The size and arrangement of the spaces depends on the materials 'on site'; for example, the uniform assemblage of particles in a sandy soil provides a very different spatial pattern from that of a cracking clay.

It is many years since Sir John Russell described soil structure as the 'architecture of the soil'. The analogy is still apt today. Just as a building consists of rooms, corridors, a framework to provide stability, a roof to protect the upper surface and coatings to prevent deterioration, the physical construction of a soil possesses equivalent components. The primary building materials in the soil consist of mineral particles, ranging in size from stones to sand and clay. Organic products and clay bind the larger particles together and in some soils calcium and iron compounds may also act as bonding agents. The strength of the bonds determines the stability of the soil and its potential to withstand the natural forces of wind and rain on the surface.

If a building is hit by a large force it can be reduced to rubble and dust, and so can a soil. However, in one important way, soil structure differs from the construction of a building; its strength depends on its water content. A soil can become malleable and plastic when wet and change shape when squeezed. These alterations may be in response to the application of mechanical force as in cultivations or to strains set up by changes in soil water content by drying and wetting, freezing and thawing. Furthermore, changes in the stability of soil can occur due to increases or decreases in the quantity or quality of binding agents such as soil organic matter.

The power available for altering the structure of the soil for better or worse has gradually increased. Originally, power was limited to that provided by one man (or woman); next, one or more draught animals were used. A major change took place in the 19th century with the introduction of steam engines anchored on the headland for pulling a plough or cultivator to and fro across the field. With the development of the internal combustion engine, the power unit once more became mobile. Tractors increasingly provided the source of power in industrial countries and since their introduction around the beginning of the 20th century they have increased over 10 fold in power and weight. Tractors are still not universally available, draught animals and manual labour provide the means of cultivation and weed control over substantial areas of the world.

When considerable force is applied directly to a lump of dry soil only a very short time is needed to break it and to disrupt soil structure; for example, a tine moving at speed through the soil or heavy rain hitting the surface. The severity of the change induced is likely to be related in some way to the magnitude of the force applied, to the area on which it was applied and to the condition of the soil itself, whether dry or wet, hard, soft or loose. Thus decisions concerning the choice and timing of landwork must be considered in relation to the properties of the soil, particularly its texture and water content, to the equipment available and also to any secondary effects that may be caused by the nature and size of the power source.

Processes which create soil structure

Before the processes of structure formation began, the surface of the soil would have been a formless mass of individual particles, for example as seen in a newly deposited river terrace, tidal mud flat or sandbank. The amount of space between them would depend on their shape and on the proportion of smaller particles available to fill in the gaps between larger particles. For example

FIGURE 4.1 The Initial Stages of Soil Structure Formation.

The initiation of soil structure in a dried out marsh pool, before the establishment of a plant cover and the introduction of organic matter from plant debris. The complex pattern of cracks was formed when water evaporated and platelets of clay in the soil moved closer together.

a beach sand may settle to a firm stable condition with a proportion of about 60% space to 40% solid grains. Some highly sandy soils have not changed much from their original state and the individual particles may be readily seen. In most soils, groups of particles have joined together to form distinct lumps, termed aggregates. Near the surface these range in size from pinhead to pea-size or larger. Further down in the soil larger, more angular blocks are commonly seen from the size of sugar cubes to the size of a spade or more. The size and shape of the aggregates depends not only on the proportion of sand, silt and clay particles present but also on the depth from the surface. To create structure in the soil, a combination of chemical, physical and biological processes is involved.

In the beginning, which for most of the U K means when the ice retreated about 12,000 years ago, soils would have been devoid of vegetation and contain little or no organic matter. At that time, the agents of landscape formation were still active in a seasonally frozen environment. As the climate warmed and the ice retreated, plants gradually became established. The major simultaneous changes following the introduction of plants would be the protection of the surface from erosive rainfall, the seasonal drying of soil and the gradual incorporation and increase in the amount of organic matter in the soil.

Both in the initial stages and later, the principal factors involved with soil structure formation are:

● cycles of drying and wetting;

● cycles of freezing and thawing;

● the binding action of roots and fungal strands

● additions of plant and faunal residues and their decomposition in the soil

Soil structure formation may begin before the introduction of plants, when the surface dries. This is shown in Figure 4.1, where an extensive and characteristic pattern of cracks has formed on the surface of a dried-out marsh pool. Such a pattern can

FIGURE 4.2 Soil Structure in an Untilled Soil.

A soil in Sherwood Forest untouched by mankind, never cropped, tilled or grazed. The size and shape of the aggregates change from fine rounded units in the upper 30 cm to larger angular blocks and then to vertical units separated by fissures which extend well below the hole dug.

occur only where there is enough clay in the soil to bring about significant shrinkage, when water is extracted from the soil. The phenomenon of shrink-swell cycles with drying and rewetting can take place only with clay and, to some extent also, with organic matter but not with sand or silt grains. Bare soil can only be dried by the atmosphere to a limited extent, typically to a spade's depth. When vegetation is present, the roots carry the drying power of the atmosphere down into the soil. Thus the depth and intensity of soil drying depends on how deep roots extend and is greater in a drier climate. In clay subsoils a characteristic pattern of deep vertical cracks is the dominant feature of structure. The cracks can reform in the same position each year along natural planes of weakness and are solely due to drying of the soil; organic matter has no direct influence. Drying in the subsoil reaches a peak around late summer when wide cracks may be seen on the surface, reaching far into the subsoil.

There is a relationship between the size of aggregates which form naturally and their depth from the surface. In the soil near the surface, the frequency of wetting and drying has an important role to play in structure formation. Freezing too has a part to play because of the disruptive expansion as water forms into ice and the dehydrating effect as crystals grow. By the physical effects of freezing and drying, thawing and wetting, the soil may be broken up to a fine almost sugar-like product. On the surface, the cycles inducing change are frequent; they may occur daily or even more often. Even a few centimetres below the surface, the frequency is much less until at some depth in the soil, only an annual wetting and drying cycle occurs.

Soils with a texture almost wholly sand have no ability to shrink as they dry, and therefore show virtually no development of structure in the subsoil. The minimum clay content for shrink-swell cycles to have any significance is probably about 12%, depending on the type of clay. Because of its small size and its internal construction, clay dominates both structure development and the field properties of soils when its concentration reaches 25% or more.

In all textures of soil, organic matter imparts stability to aggregates. This action is due partly to the direct weaving and

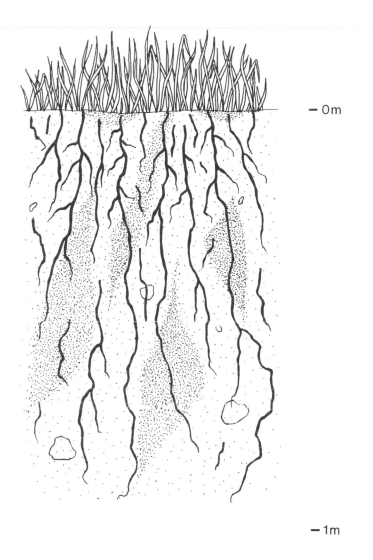

— 0m

— 1m

FIGURE 4.3 Deep Rooting in a Sandy Loam Soil.

Some soils do not crack on drying so the development of structure is weak in the subsoil; a soil of high quality, sandy loam in texture, with roots of the cereal plants extending to a depth of over 1 m.

binding effects of roots and fungal strands and partly to the indirect effects of soil humus (complex organic residues derived from the breakdown of plant roots, stems and leaves). In cultivated soils this influence is most evident to the depth disturbed regularly by cultivation. In permanent pastures the influence of organic matter may be much deeper, as much as 40 cm or more if the soil is well drained; if poorly drained the organic matter tends to accumulate as a shallow layer 15 − 20 cm deep. Soil humus is able to form flexible bridging links between sand particles and hold them together, particularly if some clay is also present. This bonding also may involve the action of microorganisms such as fungi and takes place more effectively where fresh additions of organic matter are decomposing. Soil structure formation in surface soils is therefore part physical, and part biological. There is also a relationship between the stability of aggregates and size of sand grains. Coarse sands with many particles betwween 1.0 and 2.0 mm in size have a small number of grains per unit volume and few points of contact between them. The relatively large size of the particles in relation to the small contact area between them means that bonding is ineffective and soils of this texture often have little or no aggregation and their structure is described as 'single grain'. An example is shown in Figure 4.4. This does not imply that there is any hazard from the lack of bonds between particles, because such soils are usually very porous and free draining; their main disadvantage is drought, due to lack of water.

As the size of sand grains decreases, the number of contact points per unit volume increases so that in very fine sands there often seems to be too little organic binding material to produce bonds of sufficient number or strength to form stable aggregates other than under permanent vegetation such as grass or forest. Weak structure as shown by surface capping is therefore a feature readily seen in arable soils with textures of fine sandy loam and very fine sandy loam. Nevertheless such soils are some of our best arable soils and have been cropped intensively for many years, despite their weak structure.

Soil structure and time

Scientific research on this aspect is weak and almost all reports are based on comparisons of 'number of years in or out of grass'. There is no doubt at all that, after a long period under grass,

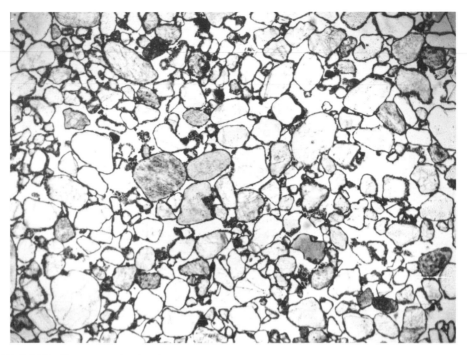

FIGURE 4.4 The Structure of a Sandy Soil.

A magnified section through a thin slice of a sandy subsoil, shows the grains in close contact with each other, so that roots may have difficulty in pushing them apart to create enough space through which to grow. The largest grains are 0.5 mm across.
(Thin section micrographs provided by E.A. Fitzpatrick)

structure is stable and well developed. This fine quality declines with arable cultivations and can be reversed by returning the land to grass. Many research reports associate these changes with soil organic matter.

What does not seem to be appreciated is that part, possibly quite a signficant part, of the difference in soil structure between grass and arable is due to the amount of physical disturbance of the soil during cultivation and also during harvesting of arable crops. Fracturing lumps of soil by impact with mechanical force breaks apart natural structure bonds very quickly. The application of high pressure by squeezing soil aggregates together can do the same.

The reverse, the creation of stable bonds, however, cannot take place over a short time scale. Months, or even tens of years may be needed. The organic bonds linking mineral particles of soil are not formed simply by mixing the two materials together. The actions of soil microorganisms and plant roots are also involved as discussed earlier in this section. The stability of structure associated with grass is therefore partly due to the high input of organic matter and partly to the lack of disturbance of the soil, to give adequate time for microbial action to provide the right material in the right place for stable bonds to develop.

Just as a crop needs time to mature, so does soil structure, but a timescale of many years is involved before maximum stability is achieved.

Soil structure and cropping

Without the intervention of man, land over most of the temperate zone would still be under forest, scrub and to a lesser extent, grass. Under such vegetation the soil at the surface would be porous and stable with a high content of organic matter. Because grass and forest alone could not provide an adequate supply of food to sustain an increasing population, land was cleared and arable cropping introduced. Initially, and for many hundreds of years, cereals were the only type of crop grown on tilled ground, other than grass.

Continuous or near continuous cropping with one species (or group of species) is regarded as disastrous by some writers, and associated with dust bowls, barley barons and man's exploitation of the land. What is not often appreciated is that there is nothing new or unique in having a long sequence of the same crop. For example, in the 18th century there are reports of cereals being grown for many years without a break in Scotland and on an Estate near Newbury. Indeed at that time few alternative crops were available. In other countries, cereals have been grown successfully and continuously for many years. However, if other crops can be grown economically there are benefits to the control of weeds, pests and diseases in having a 'break' from a long sequence of cereals.

For countless generations, some crops have been regarded as having 'good' effects on the soil , others 'bad'. Good in this context implies that certain soil characteristics have been improved, or at least have been maintained, as a result of growing a particular crop, bad, the reverse. A distinction must be made between nutritional or biological effects that a crop (or the residues it leaves behind) may have and any effects associated with the the physical properties of the soil. In addition it is not possible to separate the direct effects of a crop and the effects due to its field management and harvest. For example, the adverse effects of potatoes on soil structure are almost wholly associated with harvester traction and the method of taking the crop off the field, whereas biological effects resulting from changes in nematode populations have a dominant role in crop rotations of potatoes with other crops.

'Alternate husbandry' or 'ley farming' was introduced in the early part of the 19th century and crop rotations then established had a dominant influence for 150 years on British agriculture and indirectly too on the British landscape. The principles on which the rotations were based became incorporated into many tenancy and valuation agreements. Briefly, these rotations had a number of objectives:

● weed control, by inclusion of a cleaning crop, potatoes or turnips;

● an accumulation of nutrients, mainly nitrogen;

● minimizing the risk of an increase in crop pests and diseases;

● maintenance of soil structure and soil organic matter by the inclusion of grass in the rotation and the return of farmyard manure to the land.

Some, but not all, of these objectives can now be achieved by other means — fertilizers replace biological and organic inputs of N; many but not all weeds, diseases and pests may be controlled by chemicals. Rotational control of some pests and diseases however, is still an effective and necessary part of soil management, in some cases backed by legislation.

Concern has been widely expressed about a deterioration in soil structure when grass or grass-arable rotations are replaced by an all-arable sequence of crops. As a result many investigations have been done, under the broad title of ley fertility experiments, and the conclusions reached may be summarised:

1. soil structure deteriorates under arable crops and improves under grass, when assessed by several tests for stability or porosity;

2. organic matter levels increase, but only very slightly after each year of grass in a rotation;

3. nutrient effects, particularly of N, can be masked by the use of fertilizers.

However, the individual management of a crop plays a large and often dominant role in the overall effect that it may have on a particular soil, rather than any inherent characteristics of the crop itself. The influence that specific crops may have on soil fertility, used in its widest sense, are outlined below. One further important point must be made: it is assumed in the assessment of the effects of a specific crop, that it has been grown well; a poor or failed area of crop will do little or nothing to benefit soil fertility or structure and may actually bring about a deterioration.

Grass: Grass is probably the only major farm crop truly native to the U K; it has an excellent and well deserved reputation for maintaining organic matter and improving structure in soils.

FIGURE 4.5 *Intense Development of Finely Aggregated Structure Under Grass.*

(Above) A combination of factors is responsible for the well developed structure after a long period in grass: large numbers of fine roots, enhanced organic matter and microbial activity, repeated cycles of drying and wetting and lack of disturbance by cultivation (SW Scotland). When grassland is ploughed, the furrow fractures into fine aggregates which crumble readily. In this example (below) from E England, the period under grass was less than a year.

This is due to its perennial nature and to the long season of growth, intense development of fine roots near the surface of the soil, the high input of root debris as a source of microbial activity and organic matter, the high intensity of drying and wetting cycles and the lack of disturbance of the soil. Some of the benefits may decline if a grass sward becomes worn out, weedy or poached. While well-grown grass may have substantial residual benefits to soil structure, experience has shown that it is very sensitive to the effects of poor structure in its early life, particularly to the presence of compact layers near to the surface.

Cereals: wheat, barley, oats and rye. Botanically these crops are members of the grass family and therefore have some characteristics in common with grass as a crop. One important difference is that cereals are not perennial, so that for almost half the growing season, there is no significant production of organic matter (i.e. at the time of sowing when the soil is bare, and at the end of the season when the land bears a ripening crop or stubble). Nevetheless, the root system is intensively developed near the soil surface and can grow to considerable depths, down to 1.6 − 2.0 m. The input of organic matter to the soil is substantial in the form of roots even if straw is removed or the stubble burnt. Provided weeds, pests and diseases can be controlled, long runs of cereals present a low risk of soil deterioration in temperate climates as long as a vigorous crop is grown. Indeed, on land cropped intensively with root crops, cereals have a good reputation as structure-improvers because of their ability to dry out the soil to depth thereby enhancing soil fracturing on clayey subsoils. A further potential benefit of cereals is that because the crop is harvested above ground, the dead stubble can remain for some months to protect the surface of the soil from erosive forces of wind and rain. Compared to root crops and potatoes, there is no disturbance of the soil between sowing and harvest apart from wheel tracks associated with the addition of chemicals.

Potatoes: To provide suitable soil to form a ridge, a deep, fine clod-free tilth is preferred which may be prepared by a combination of autumn landwork, winter weathering and intensive spring cultivation. In late wet springs, there is a risk that soil may be damaged by working and planting while the land is wet. At harvest, lifting and transporting the crop presents few problems from soils that are no more than slightly wet. The major hazard is from extensive tracking of the surface by the harvester and by pulling off loaded trailers in wet conditions when deep ruts and severe compaction of the soil may occur. On land that is clayey or slow draining, and in wetter areas, early harvest should be planned to minimize the damage to the soil. If cultivation is not done to break up compact tracks, any subsequent rain may run down ruts to form pools in lower parts of the field.

Potatoes are relatively shallow rooted, usually reaching a maximum depth of 60 − 80 cm. The period of growth is short and the residues of organic matter added to the soil are relatively low. However, any long term detrimental effect on soil structure is likely to originate not from a decline in organic matter, but from mechanical damage to the soil during harvest.

Sugar beet: There are many similarities to the points made concerning potatoes although sugar beet and most other root crops have a longer growing season and are usually harvested much later. Less soil is disturbed to detach the crop from the soil compared with lifting and separating potato tubers, so the mechanical risks are not so severe from the harvester itself, but there is often a greater mass of crop to carry off the field, sometimes in wet conditions. Therefore, any risk to soil structure is likely to be strongly related to the soil wetness at harvest. Sugar beet is deep rooting, though compact layers of soil can readily inhibit the downward growth of roots. Because of its deep rooting habit and growth through summer and well into autumn, soil drying may be deep and intensive, giving benefits to subsoil structure and to subsequent drainage.

Oil seed rape: When autumn sown, much of the pre-winter growth develops below ground as carbohydrate reserves accrue in the roots. To enable an extensive deep root system to develop in autumn, compact layers of soil should not be present, and while a fine seedbed is needed for the small seeds, any surface capping that occurs after drilling may inhibit emergence. The roots are not so fine as cereals but the benefits to soil structure and soil organic matter residues are likely to be similar.

Peas and beans: In common with other legumes, these crops are well known for their N-fixing properties. They do not appear to have many benefits or hazards to soil structure. The organic matter residues are likely to be relatively small and would decompose quickly because of their higher nitrogen content. The major risk would be from crops grown under contract for vining and therefore with a short period for harvest during which quality is high: if heavy viners and associated equipment operate to fulfil a contract when soils are wet, compaction can be severe. Because legumes have only one tap root they are more at risk from soil compaction problems than cereals; they are also particularly sensitive to lack of aeration.

Vegetables: The major risk crops are those harvested from the soil under wet conditions, (e.g. root vegetables, leeks) particularly if heavy harvesters and trailers for transport off the field are used. Severe and deep compaction can occur. Efficient field drainage is an essential prerequisite except on naturally free-draining soils. Crops with the saleable fraction above ground (e.g. lettuce, Brussels sprouts, cabbages, spinach) present less risk of damage particularly if harvested in summer, by hand or with light machinery, whether for cutting or transport off the field. As for other root crops, any surface tracks made during harvest should be broken up by cultivation before rain falls to run down tracks and collect as wet patches in low areas.

Forage crops: kale, rape and turnips. These crops are broadcast or drilled usually in late spring when soil conditions should be favourable for seedbed preparation except on wetter land. They may be grazed direct or removed from the field for feeding elsewhere. The risks to the soil depend on its state when harvest or grazing is done. Forage roots may be used from November right through winter until the following April, or even later in upland areas. Grazing is more often with sheep than cattle and any poaching damage would be shallow and should be subsequently removed by ploughing. When turnips are lifted regularly over winter, severe tracking from harvesters and loaded trailers can occur.

Green manure crops: grass, rape, soft turnips or mustard and sometimes a mixture, usually sown after cereal harvest (or

FIGURE 4.6 The Importance of Post-harvest Tillage (i).

Contrast a dry headland with surface tracks broken up soon after they were made, after harvesting roots in early autumn, with unrelieved surface compaction on a similar soil nearby where harvest was much later and tracks are impervious and water-filled. (Photographed on the same day in November).

even before) for grazing off or ploughing-in during late autumn or winter. This practice was common when sheep were kept on arable farms, but is now mainly confined to land intensely used where the benefit to structure carries a premium to the following crop. One advantage of green manuring over leaving the land in stubble, is that the growing crop takes up some of the residues of nitrate from the soil, thereby reducing the risk of their loss by leaching.

Fallow: In times past, a period of 'rest' or 'fallow' when no crop was grown and the land kept clean of weeds, was a well established practice designed to reduce the population of weeds, pests and diseases. During the fallow period, usually in summer, there would be no or very little input of organic matter. The decomposition of organic residues in the soil would continue so that the next crop could benefit from the accumulation of nitrates. However, in context of soil structure and present-day farm practices, a fallow presents a considerable hazard and cannot be recommended. If no plants are present, neither crop nor weed, then soil drying is limited to surface evaporation, and the subsoil would remain moist all summer. This effect is illustrated in Figure 6.1. Clays would not crack to any extent under a fallow. All soils would be quickly re-wetted to field capacity by only a small amount of rain. As a result, cultivation in late summer or autumn would invariably be done in quite wet soils. After a late wet spring there is a temptation to leave land fallow for the summer in preparation for early autumn sowing of cereals or oil seed rape. However, if soil compaction was partly responsible for the wet condition of the land in spring, there would be no improvement under a fallow. It would be much better in such circumstances to sow a crop, any crop, in order to gain the benefit of deeper soil drying through transpiration of water through the green crop, thereby making possible more effective remedial cultivations. For such a contingency the crop selected may be anything inexpensive, convenient to sow and easy to deal with afterwards; grass, and cereals are possibilities as these can be broadcast if necessary with little or no cultivation. Another problem that may affect a bare fallow, is that the soil surface is unprotected and exposed to rain batter, which may lead to soil capping and possibly to erosion.

Table 4.1

Summary of relative effects of crops on input of organic matter and risk of damage to soil structure

	Relative benefits:			possible adverse effects
	to soil organic matter	to soil structure	other benefits	
Grass	very good	very good	surface protected	poaching damage by grazing livestock
Autumn cereals	moderate	good	stubble protection	erosion down wheel tracks
Spring cereals	moderate	moderate	stubble protection	erosion down wheeltracks
Potatoes	poor	poor		high risk of soil compaction when harvested in wet conditions
Sugar beet	poor (with tops ploughed in moderate)	poor	late growth, deep rooting	late harvest on wet land
Oilseed rape	moderate	good	stubble protection	as cereals
Peas/beans	poor	poor	N residues	risk of soil damage if harvested when land is wet
Vegetables	poor to moderate	poor	—	summer or hand-harvested, little risk; autumn or winter harvested by machine, severe risk of soil damage
Forage roots	good	moderate to poor	—	risk of damage if wet when grazed or harvested
Green manuring	poor	moderate to poor	conservation of nitrate	benefit to structure depends on soil conditions when grazed or ploughed in
Fallow	no input	none or negative	reduction of weeds, pests & diseases	no drying of the subsoil

The same points apply to any uncropped area of land whether of fallow by design, a patch of crop failure, a wet hollow or a bare headland.

Deterioration of soil structure

Soil structure deteriorates when aggregates are deformed by the application of pressure. The force applied may come externally from tractors, trailers and other machinery, from grazing livestock, from the impact of rain or, internally, from the breaking out of trapped air when aggregates are flooded, as illustrated in Figure 5.2.

Under natural conditions in temperate climates, deterioration of soil structure would be rare; beneath scrub, forest or pasture the only significant change would be along tracks used regularly by foraging animals and at drinking holes or where cover had been removed by fire. When mankind intervenes to grow crops of his choice, the changes as far as structure are concerned may be examined in two groups: the first deals with those associated with a net reduction in the concentration of organic matter in the soil on the land surface; the second with changes in physical properties resulting from the reaction of the soil to an applied force, i.e. soil compaction or smearing.

At the outset it is important to appreciate that a decline in the quality of structure does not invariably lead to a reduction in the yields of crops or grass. Indeed any arable crop, however well grown, will introduce some degree of deterioration in aggregate stability when compared to natural undisturbed grassland or forest. The question to consider is how to identify the point at which deterioration induces significant hazards to crop production or to the capability of the land. Erosion, which is usually the result of a deterioration in structure, is discussed in Chapter 9.

A decline in organic matter

The factors influencing the concentration of organic matter in the soil are discussed in Chapter 5. Climate and soil texture have a dominant influence. Nevertheless when compared to grass, arable land in a similar situation will almost always have a lower concentration of organic matter in the topsoil. Part of this decline may be due to removal of the crop, part to dilution as a result of deep working and part to the increased rate of decomposition as a result of the physical fracturing, mixing and aeration during cultivation. However, much is due to the fact that when annual arable crops are grown there are one or two periods of the year when there is no production of organic matter derived from plant growth − one during seedbed preparation until emergence and the other before and after harvest. This shortfall may be compensated by the addition of animal manures or growing a green manure crop. As discussed in Chapter 1, most crops grow at a similar rate under the same conditions, so any difference in gross dry matter production between crops would be principally due to differences in the period of active growth; this aspect and others associated with individual crops was discussed in the last section on soil structure and cropping.

The stability of soil aggregates has been assessed in many experiments which have compared periods of arable cropping with periods of grass. The results are clear; under arable cropping aggregate stability declines, and under grass it increases. However, it is also clear that this unequivocal conclusion has not prevented farmers from growing arable crops continuously and successfully without the benefits of grass in the rotation. How can this apparent conflict of evidence be resolved? The salient point is to establish whether the lower soil organic matter concentration and lower aggregate stability reach critical values at which it becomes difficult or impossible to continue to grow arable crops alone. For almost all soils in Britain the evidence to date is that the critical point has not been reached, and would be unlikely to be reached, as long as cereals are the predominant arable crop. This should not be interpreted as a complacent conclusion that soil structure problems do not exist; they do, and may be increasing. However, field experience suggests that farmers are generally able to continue arable cropping on soils which exhibit soil structure problems, by a combination of skilful cultivations and the inclusion of recuperative crops in the rotation. This was broadly the conclusion of the Strutt Report in 1970. Individual fields, or parts of fields, may present problems as discussed in some of the examples in Chapters 8, 9 and 10.

When a regular sequence of crops is grown for some time, the organic matter concentration in a particular soil will settle to a steady value, with small variations due to the influence of individual crops and seasonal weather. It is this equilibrium value or the lowest value in a cycle of cropping which determines the related long term structural condition of the soil. In the context of cropping type and organic matter, field experience is as valid as a test based on laboratory analysis for soil organic matter content or soil structure stability.

A deterioration of soil structure stability may be observed in the field as a splitting off of the individual particles of soil from aggregates, the bonds holding them together becoming so weak that they can no longer withstand disruptive forces. In practice many soils do not show any signs of this condition; it is restricted mainly to soils which contain a high proportion of fine sand, very fine sand or silt. It is these soils which may form a crust or cap on the surface when exposed to heavy rain or when flooded. Another common sign of weak structure is the presence of pale coloured fine sand grains, often collected together in thin veins or layers near the surface or at the base of cultivations.

Whenever signs are detected of weak surface structure, (i.e. surface capping or particle detachment) the objective of soil management should be to ensure that no further deterioration takes place and that erosion does not occur. Protection of the surface is a key factor as it is the surface that bears the impact of rain. In a heavy storm raindrops may have a velocity of 9 m/sec and the impact pressure of such raindrops at the soil surface can be as much as 60 bar (900 psi). On bare soil the aggregates have to absorb the energy but not if a crop or stubble covers the surface.

Measures to protect the surface and to avoid or alleviate the effects of rainfall-batter include reducing to a minimum the period when bare soil is exposed to rain, keeping cultivations as shallow as feasible to retain crop residues in a smaller volume of soil thereby increasing, albeit slightly, the organic matter concentration, reducing the number of cultivations, also, if necessary, increasing the proportion of autumn cereals in the rotation and reducing the proportion of root crops. Under intensive horticultural management it is possible to encounter serious slumping and hard setting problems (see Chapter 8) where sudden wetting even without the addition of the mechanical battering by rain can trigger structural collapse.

FIGURE 4.7 Contrasts in Surface Structure.

On a well structured stable soil, the surface absorbed rain with minimal disintegration, and a slight over-winter cap fractured as the soil dried in spring (above). Contrast this with a weakly structured soil of the same texture where the surface aggregates on a headland have disintegregated under heavy rain to form a continuous thin cap, but showing well preserved structure beneath.

In subsoils organic matter has a negligble effect on structure formation and stability so any changes in organic matter content as a result of different crops or grass are unlikely to have effects of practical significance in the subsoil. Of greater relevance in the subsoil is the need to encourage deep rooting and to provide good drainage.

Soil over-compaction

Soil over-compaction is a widespread condition, not just of the present, but of times past too, long before the advent of the 100 HP tractor. It is created by a combination of pressure and sliding forces as they are applied to the soil from a wide range of sources: for example, from driving wheels, trailed wheels, plough soles, disc edges, rotary blades, the hooves of draught horses or grazing livestock. When applied to firm, dry or slightly moist soil such forces will be resisted by the soil without it being changed, or will be expended almost wholly in cutting or fracturing the soil. When applied to soft, moist, plastic and malleable soil, compression or smearing occurs. After such a change soil is reduced in volume, increased in density and is less permeable to air, water and roots.

The way in which a soil reacts to the application of pressure depends on the texture of the soil, how wet it is, how hard it is, its depth below the surface and also on the shape and contact area of the source of the pressure.

Soils which are dominated by sand are permeable and usually contain large pores and have no plastic properties. As a result, compaction is usually less obvious but can nevertheless occur leading particularly to a difficulty in root penetration. In subsoils which consist wholly of medium sand, fine sand or very fine sand, roots have difficulty in penetrating more than a few centimetres. In the author's experience, this phenomenon, illustrated in Figure 4.8, is surprizingly widespread and the reason for it is not fully understood. Lack of moisture in the sand does not seem to be responsible as the condition has been observed in moist sands; neither do high density nor cementing seem to be involved. One possible explanation is that despite their obvious porosity, sands in their undisturbed state are rigid because of particles interlocking and they cannot readily move apart to accommodate the growing root. A thickened stubby

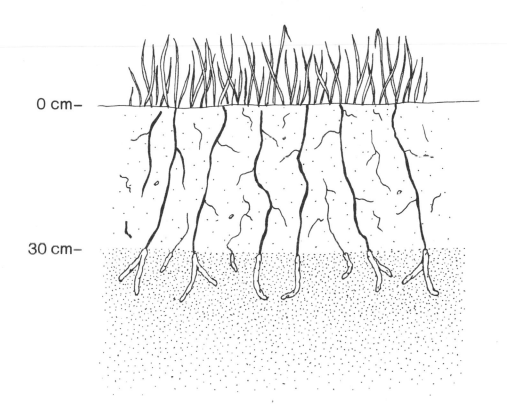

0 cm–

30 cm–

FIGURE 4.8 Restricted Growth of Roots in Sand.

Even without any visible signs of compaction, roots are often able to penetrate only a few centimetres into sand; where this occurs they swell and distort as they enter the sand.

appearance is often seen on the last few centimetres of root when this phenomenon is present. Thus sandy soils may be droughty both because of lack of water held by the sand and also by a restriction to root depth.

Only very sandy soils are completely without plastic properties and most soils contain enough clay to be plastic when wet, that is, they can be deformed to a new shape by pressure, which brings about significant changes in appearance and properties. The imprint of the applying force such as a cleated tyre may be moulded into the soil and remain there for months or even a year or more; water entry may be restricted giving rise to a water-logged layer above the compact soil; air entry may also be restricted producing anaerobic pockets in the compressed soil, root entry may be inhibited with few growing into the compact soil and some roots may be seen as a web on the upper face of the compact layer.

A hard soil of whatever texture has considerable internal strength and may not react in any way to pressure until enough force is applied to fracture the soil; loosening rather than compaction is the result. When very dry, the force required to break the soil may be considerable and beyond the capability of all but the most powerful equipment. As a dry soil rewets the internal strength reduces and less force is required to break it. Just before it contains enough water to be plastic a soil reaches a weak state when lumps of it break with a minimum of force − the ideal state for safe cultivation.

The above paragraphs are an oversimplification of this aspect of soil mechanics but serve to illustrate a key point; the water content is the critical factor which influences the reaction of the soil to pressure. If dry, loads can be carried safely without compaction. If slightly moist and lumps can be broken apart easily by hand then load carrying is rather more at risk but cultivation can be effective and efficient. If too wet (soft and plastic when handled) then compaction is inevitable from any pressure applied.

It might be thought that spreading the weight of a heavy load over a larger contact area with wide tyres, double wheels or tracks reduces compaction damage. Up to a point, this is true, especially near to the soil surface. However, a large contact area also ensures that the compaction is felt at a greater depth. As more of this compaction can then be below plough depth great care is needed whenever heavy axle loads are involved in considering whether there is likely to be compaction at depth.

The greatest risks of serious compaction occur when landwork of any type is required in wet soil conditions: preparing seedbeds in late wet springs or early wet autumns, harvesting in wet conditions particularly of roots with a heavy weight to transport off the field, any work in normal seasons in poorly drained or wet areas. Timing, in relation to field moisture conditions, is therefore the critical factor and any action to ensure drier conditions at times when land work cannot be put off will reduce the risks of compaction. Field drainage is obviously a key technique and also any action which helps rain to infiltrate the soil and not flow down slopes to collect in low areas.

It is vital to appreciate that a single inadvertent, misapplied or unavoidable action taken under wet field conditions may undo many years of careful soil management, and furthermore may take several years to restore.

It is also important to add that soils of all types may be adversely affected by compaction, none are immune.

Chapter 5 SOIL ORGANIC MATTER

Successful cropping using nutrient film or other hydroponic techniques demonstrates that organic matter as such is not essential for plant growth. However, in soil, organic matter is regarded by some as the vital and essential link controlling soil productivity; to others, no more than a minor soil component of which the significance faded with the advent of modern farming techniques. The truth lies somewhere between these extreme views. What is not controversial is the fact that soil organic matter is highly complex and its components have only been partially identified. What is also clear is that the age of organic matter in the soil ranges widely from very recent additions which may be no more than a few hours old to ancient humus more than a thousand years old. The amount of organic matter present in a soil depends on the accumulated balance between the quantity added each year and the rate of decay. Many factors other than cropping or manuring are involved such as climate, soil texture and aeration. Organic matter has many important effects on soil properties: soil structure, particularly its stability, soil water reserves, soil colour, nutrient supply, particularly nitrogen, phosphorus and sulphur, and leaching of nutrients.

Origins of soil organic matter

Organic matter in soils is largely derived from plants. It may originate directly from plants grown in a soil or indirectly from plants grown elsewhere when manure, slurry, sewage or other organic product is applied. If no manures are used, the amount added directly to the soil each year depends on how much was formed above ground by photosynthesis and on how much was removed by harvest and by decay before incorporation. The total amount of organic matter formed appears to depend on the length of time a crop is actively growing. A typical value for the production of organic matter in average conditions in lowland Britain would be about 200 kg/ha dry matter per day. In the south of the country, despite a higher intensity of solar radiation there is proportionally no greater production of crop dry matter compared to the north, mainly because of an increased rate of plant respiration in the higher temperatures of the south.

At harvest many parts of the plant are rejected and left in or on the soil, as straw, haulm, tops or roots. Some are returned after consumption by animals, directly as voided faeces or after a period of storage. Whatever the sources, their contribution to soil organic matter and to other soil properties depends on the quantity added, when it is added, its location in the soil, and its quality as an energy and nutrient supply for the growth of microorganisms and other life in the soil.

The decomposition of organic materials in soil

Soils contain many different forms of microbial and other life in substantial numbers, as shown in Table 5.1. In a typical soil, the majority of microorganisms remain in the same position and move only when their surroundings move as in root extension, water movement, cultivation and transfer by earthworms, beetles and other insects. The numbers of microorganisms can decline sharply in adverse conditions, and many can change to resistant forms that can remain dormant for long periods. In response to favourable conditions numbers can increase rapidly, particularly where there is a supply of suitable food. One such location is in the immediate vicinity of live roots. Here, there is a continual supply of carbohydrate derived from the leakage of roots. Up to 15% of all the carbohydrate fixed by the plant is released in this way. This leaked material is all readily decomposed by microorganisms, and is an important source of carbon for the formation of bonds to stabilise soil aggregates. When plant residues such as leaves and stems are incorporated into the soil and roots that are already in the soil die, decay begins. Soil inhabiting insects, larvae and worms nibble at and reduce the size of plant residues, and also may drag them into or through the soil, This action exposes more of the plant to microbial attack. Cultivation too, stimulates microbial activity and organic matter decomposition, by shattering and mixing soil and by incorporating surface residues.

The plant residues contain many different organic compounds, sugars, starches, proteins, waxes and other highly

Table 5.1 Approximate numbers of some organisms in a typical agricultural surface soil and their mass in a depth of 15 cm

	numbers per gram dry soil	mass kg/ha
Bacteria	100 million	1600
Actinomycetes	2 million	1600
Fungi	0.2 million	2000
Algae	25,000	320
Protozoa	30,000	380
Nematodes	1.5	120
Earthworms	1 per kg	800

complex molecules. The easiest to decompose are those providing a ready source of energy for microbial life such as simple sugars; others are more resistant to attack, provide poor sources of energy and may remain undecomposed or only partly decomposed for some time. As less and less of the original source remains, numbers of active microorganisms will fall as their food supply dwindles, and as what is left is more difficult to decompose. The main product of organic decomposition is carbon dioxide but it is the residue left behind which affects many physical and chemical properties of soils. The final product is a complex organic material, termed soil humus, relatively resistant to further attack by microorganisms. What is surprising is that soil humus possesses many similar properties over a broad range of climatic regions, considering the very diverse plant materials and animal manures which are added to the soil.

The rate of decomposition of organic additions to the soil is dependent on the environment within the soil: temperature, water content, pH, aeration and soil texture are all involved. Temperature has a predominant influence; the optimum for decomposition in temperate climates is $25-30°C$ and little decomposition takes place below 10°C. In cooler northern Britain this results in distinctly higher levels of soil organic matter compared to the warmer south. Wetness also has a significant influence, which is independent of temperature; the ultimate example is peat formation in waterlogged conditions which can take place at any temperature from tundra to the tropics.

Many microorganisms capable of breaking down organic matter become less active as acidity increases, so that acid soils below pH 5.0 usually contain greater concentrations of soil organic matter. In arable land where pH values should be maintained near or above neutrality, organic decomposition will not be restricted by acidity.

Soil texture also has a significant effect on soil organic matter concentration, and as the clay content of mineral soils increases, so does soil organic matter. This relationship appears to be derived mainly from the fact that some of the humus can combine with clay to form stable complex structures, where the organic matter is protected from further attack by soil microorganisms.

Several of these complex relationships are shown in Table 5.2 which illustrates a strong effect of clay content on organic matter levels taken after a long period of similar cropping at six MAFF Experimental Husbandry Farms. The relative influence of cropping, i.e. comparing grass with arable, can be seen to have a smaller effect than soil texture; the effect of climate is less discernible because of the relatively small variation in the climate between the six farms.

While the main product of organic decomposition in soils is carbon dioxide, mineral nutrients are also released to make an important contribution to plant nutrition. The amounts of greatest significance are nitrogen, phosphorus and sulphur but all elements contained in the original plant residues will be released as it decomposes.

Incorporation of organic residues is not always beneficial; if straw is packed closely around grain in the seedbed, toxic acids produced in the early stages of decomposition may hinder germination. If residues which provide a good substrate for microbial growth are incorporated under wet conditions and become surrounded by dense soil, anaerobic conditions may develop with subsequent adverse effects on crop growth and nitrogen supply. Incorporation of straw can also lead to a temporary shortage of available nitrogen for the crop due to prior use by microbial decomposers.

The age and activity of organic matter in soils

At any one time in the soil, there are likely to be organic materials of a wide range of ages from recently added or living plant structures to partly decomposed organic matter through to well decomposed material and to the resistant end product, soil humus. In addition, living microbes are a significant proportion and may comprise 1% or more of the total amount of soil organic matter present in soil.

The level of organic matter present in any soil is thus rarely constant. The more active part is subject to short term fluctuations, with additions and decay taking place simultaneously, sometimes one, sometimes the other, being greater. By far the largest portion is relatively inert and changes only slowly.

The major fraction of organic matter is very old, and must be either virtually incapable of further decomposition or protected physically from microbial attack. In either case, the old material is unlikely to be contributing significantly to properties associated with active forms of organic matter such as soil structure stability. Evidence to support this view is the rapid decline in aggregate stability when old grassland is ploughed out and the sharp increase in the same property when arable land is returned to grass. After a few years under grass, organic matter may rise by say 0.1% but the stability of soil aggregates may rise by a factor of two or three.

Organic matter and soil structure

Until they decompose, plant residues may benefit soil physical properties by protecting the surface from rain batter. There may also be benefits to surface drainage, due to the gaps and air pockets surrounding recently incorporated straw and other rigid crop residues.

FIGURE 5.1 Distintegration of Surface Aggregates after Heavy Rain.

A soil with structure on the surface weak enough to disintegrate in heavy rain and where water has ponded: field view and close up showing fine sand grains separated from the aggregates.

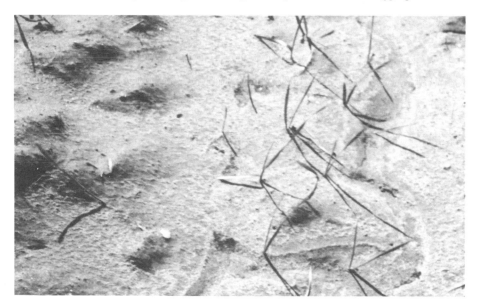

Some groups of carbohydrates known as polysaccharides are associated with the bonding of particles into soil structure aggregates. These organic gums are not present in the same form in plants, so that decay processes are required to generate them. What also appears to happen is that when these organic bonds of structure are broken, either by physical fracture or decomposition by microorganisms, the products cannot reform and new sources of organic matter are needed to provide new bonds and to restore the structure. In addition to microbial polysaccharides acting as agents of structural stability, the filamentous fungi are known to enmesh soil particles and further enhance aggregate formation. A sterile soil is therefore unlikely to provide organic material in forms suitable for the creation of stable aggregates and the expression 'a soil hasn't much life in it' may be an apt description for both structure formation and microbial acitivity.

Increasing soil organic matter

While soil organic matter is an important component influencing many soil properties the concentration in the soil is related to both the rate of addition and the rate of decomposition. If it is judged necessary to increase soil organic matter, this can best be done by increasing the input, since the rate of decay is mainly due to natural agencies over which little or no control can be exerted. To bring about an increase may require a change in cropping or the retention of more of the residues in the soil. A period under grass is the best means, and for each year under grass, soil organic matter may increase by up to about 0.1%. This rate of increase will not continue indefinitely and it could take 10 years or more to approach a new higher stable equlibrium value. Even for short periods of 1 or 2 years, grass can lead to a marked increase in the stability of aggregates, even though the increase in organic matter may be small. On many arable farms, the introduction of a period under grass may not be acceptable or economically viable, though grass for seed production is grown in some predominantly arable areas. Other members of the grass family, namely cereals, are grown to provide seed on over 80% of the arable land in Britain; these are wheat and barley with smaller areas of oats, rye, triticale and durum. While not so good as grass in increasing soil organic matter, cereals are not far behind, particularly those sown early in autumn so that they can generate organic matter from much of the late season solar radiation. Irrespective of whether straw is burnt or not, cereal crops leave behind significant amounts of organic matter in the soil in their roots, up to about half of the total crop dry matter produced. An autumn sown 'green manure' crop would also provide a protective cover, though the ultimate increase in soil organic matter may be negligible when the residues are ploughed in the following spring.

Addition of farm manure and other bulky organic manures may also increase soil organic matter but to produce significant changes frequent and heavy applications are necessary. The results of a large number of field trials testing bulky organic manures over many years have shown that when applied at agricultural rates the value of these manures depended to a large extent on their content of plant nutrients. However, some of these trials have also shown distinct improvements in structure and increases in soil organic matter from the use of farm manure.

Whatever the merits of farm manure, it is not now available in most arable areas, so that its use to improve soil organic matter even if unequivocally established, could not be adopted as a general practice. The availability of other bulky organics such as compost or sewage products is limited and their use would be restricted by transport and spreading costs. Organic additions in the form of farm slurries may be made but their use is dominated by their high water content (90 − 98%) and in some cases by their content of potentially toxic metals. Their value is regarded primarily as nutrient sources and very high rates of application are inadvisable because of the risks of nutrient imbalance or excess and also to pollution of ground water or streams. A thick layer of slurry left on the surface of grass may smother the leaves and reduce the rate of growth. When applied to bare soil at high rates there is a risk that the surface structure may be damaged or capped, particularly if a rain gun is used to apply the slurry.

One significant disadvantage of all bulky manures is that large applications are needed to provide benefits, and hence heavy loads must be pulled across the land with consequent risks of soil over-compaction under wheeltracks.

'Organic fertilizers', that are applied in small quantities are not likely to have any significant effect on soil organic matter levels. After a correction for the fraction decomposed, any ultimate addition to soil organic matter is likely to be less than 20% of that applied by the end of the first season. For example, after an application of 300 kg/ha of an organic fertilizer, a residue of, say, 60 kg would have little influence when diluted with 2500 t/ha of topsoil, a typical value.

An alternative to increasing the input of organic materials, is to attempt to utilize more effectively the amount that is added. This can be done by retaining organic additions whether of roots, stubble or manures, close to the surface. The reason for this is that the stability of structure is related to the concentration of organic matter in the soil tilth at the surface and not to the total quantity present in the soil as a whole. There are several steps which can be taken to effect an improvement. For example limiting or reducing the depth of incorporating residues, and avoiding deep ploughing to bring up raw subsoil which would dilute the organic concentration on the surface,

Critical levels of organic matter

Many farmers are rightly concerned to know whether or not their soils contain enough organic matter. No direct answer can be given by determining the amount present in the soil because of the effects of factors involved outwith the control of soil management, such as climate and soil texture. For example a concentration of 2.6% organic matter may be relatively low in a soil of high clay content in Northamptonshire but the same concentration would be regarded as extremely high not far away in a Nottinghamshire sand. Despite the limitations of interpretation of soil organic matter figures, there is merit in regular analysis being done, so that changes in the same field can be followed. If this is to be done, considerable care must be taken when sampling the soil so that dilution and loosening effects of cultivation do not distort the results, and that truly comparative figures can be obtained.

There is one further difficulty in assessing critical levels of organic matter by measuring the total amount present; only a fraction of the total is actively concerned with other soil properties such as soil structure. There is no simple method as yet of identifying the active fraction. The apparent high levels of total soil organic matter in cooler and wetter areas may give a false impression of security, because much of this may be largely

FIGURE 5.2 The Effect of Waterlogging on Soil Structure.
Waterlogging alone may cause aggregates to collapse so that a continuous slurried cap is formed: field view and close-up of capped and unaffected structure a short distance away.

inert and contribute little to the active fraction. If the active fraction declined under intensive cropping, signs of structure problems may occur when levels of total organic matter remained apparently high.

Another approach to the question of soil organic matter is to monitor critical features of the physical condition of the soil associated with organic matter, for example the stability of structure in the topsoil. By this means it should be possible to detect any signs of deterioration. This would be most likely in soils of susceptible textures, loamy sands, sandy loam, fine sandy loam, very fine sandy loam and silty soils. The initial manifestation of a decline may be seen as surface capping, separation of fine sand grains or erosion, all features occurring on or within the surface layer of the soil.

Once signs of weak surface structure have been noted, the next question to consider is what effects, if any, are being seen in crop emergence or growth. Typical problems may be shown as weak or erratic crop emergence as a result of the creation of a sealed cap on the surface which may be devoid of air when wet and very hard when dry.

As soon as crop problems arise, or even before they occur on intensively cropped land, intense effort should be made to look at all possible causes of a decline in structure stability as well as a decline in organic matter. For example, excessive use of power cultivators, deep ploughing, water collecting in low areas or subsoil compaction may all contribute to weakened structure. Careful soil examination is required to identify the cause of any deterioration and to formulate plans for recovery.

A reversal of the downward trend may require firm action accompanied by a fundamental change in farming practice. This is most likely to involve a change in crop rotation, with the introduction of grass as a break crop, or an increase in the proportion of cereals, particularly autumn sown and well established with a good protective cover before winter. A review of cultivation practice may also be relevant to determine whether more efficient, less damaging procedures can be adopted. The selection of crops or varieties which are harvested earlier and under drier soil conditions can also lead to improvements.

Despite apparent reassurances that there is no cause for concern, it is also true to say that there is no room for complacency. Organic matter is a key component influencing soil structure and crop nutrition. Management of the soil must be directed firmly at conserving soil organic matter and maintaining as high a concentration as practicable in the zone where it exerts most influence in the soil, that is, on the surface. Regular monitoring of both the concentration of organic matter and of the physical properties it influences should be as much a part of routine examination and analysis as tests for soil pH, P and K.

Table 5.2 Concentration of soil organic matter (%) after 17 years' cropping under different rotations at six ADAS Experimental Husbandry Farms

	continuous arable	3-yr ley grazed 3-yr arable	mean annual rainfall (mm)	clay content (%)
Boxworth (Cambridgeshire)	3.31	3.70	550	45
Bridget's (Hampshire)	3.83	4.26	780	25
Gleadthorpe (Notts.)	1.54	1.81	600	5
High Mowthorpe (Yorkshire)	3.40	3.85	750	29
Rosemaund (Herefordshire)	2.63	2.93	650	26
Trawscoed (Dyfed)	5.64	5.98	1180	27
Mean	3.39	3.75		

Note: care is needed when examining figures for organic matter in soils, because in some reports they are expressed as 'organic carbon'. All figures in this text are given as 'organic matter' (which are greater than those for organic carbon by a factor of 1.728)

Chapter 6

WATER IN SOILS

Water is essential for all forms of life. Most of that which the plant requires is absorbed from the soil by its roots and as water is extracted by plants the soil dries; if there is not enough water to meet the demand, plant growth suffers.

Available water

The water content of soils may vary from a few per cent to 50% or more (organic soils and peats may contain even greater amounts). However, not all of this water is available for use by a crop. The most easily available is that loosely held in a moist soil. In order to compare the availability of water in different soils, two standard terms are used. One is field capacity, the other, permanent wilting point. Field capacity is defined as the water present in a soil that has been saturated and allowed to drain until all drainage has ceased. The permanent wilting point (PWP) is the amount of water left in a soil when it is so dry that plants growing in it wilt and do not recover. For convenience in laboratory tests for PWP, water is expelled from the soil by the application of high pressure (in this case 15 bar); the water then remaining corresponds to the permanent wilting point.

The difference in water content between the two, field capacity and permanent wilting point, is termed available water. Not all of this water is equally available; the drier a soil becomes, the more difficult it becomes for a plant to extract water. An approximate analogy to the availability of water in a soil may be demonstrated with a dish cloth: when taken out of a bowl of water the cloth is saturated and water drips from it when hung on a line; when dripping stops the cloth is at the equivalent of field capacity; squeeze it very hard by hand to wring out water — equivalent to the amount available; the remainder which cannot be squeezed out and could be removed only by drying thoroughly is analogous to the permanent wilting point.

Soils differ in the amount of water they contain. Those holding most available water are very fine sandy loams, silty soils and peats which explains part of the reason for the high value of these soils for cropping in drier areas. In mineral soils, organic matter influences available water in two ways. First, it may increase directly the amount of available water. As a rough guide 1% of soil organic matter could increase the amount of available water in the top 25 cm of soil by about 1 mm. Secondly, and probably a greater influence, is due to the effect that organic matter has on the stability of structure and the porosity of soils. Most topsoils contain about 10% more available water than subsoils of the same texture, except for very sandy soils which have similar amounts in both topsoil and subsoil. By far the greatest influence on water available is that of particle size and type. Coarse sand grains can hold very little water between them at field capacity; fine sands, very fine sands and silty soils hold much more and can release a high proportion of this for use by plants; clays hold a high amount at field capacity but only a limited proportion of this may be withdrawn from the soil by plant roots.

Available water in soils may be expressed as per cent by volume, or as mm per unit depth of soil. The values range from 7 to 9% for coarse sandy soils (7 to 9 mm in 10 cm depth of soil) to about 25% for very fine sandy loams (25 mm in 10 cm depth of soil); peats may have higher values, up to 30%. While clays can retain relatively large amounts of water, the available fraction ranges from about 17% to 20%, and is strongly influenced by the structure of the soil.

The total amount of available water accessible to a crop is dependent not only on particle size and organic matter but also on the depth of soil through which roots can grow. Only a limited amount of water can move upwards from moist soil below root depth to drier soil near the roots, so that 'depth of soil' virtually means 'depth of rooting'. Therefore anything which creates a barrier to roots (such as dense soil or rocks) cuts off access to available water reserves below.

Water loss from bare soil

If soil is bare with neither weed nor crop showing through, water is lost from the surface only by evaporation. The amount converted from liquid to vapour depends on heat from the sun, on wind and on the dryness of the air. In good drying conditions in lowland Britain, a wet soil surface soon appears dry after rain and the loss in a day will be of the order of 3 − 5 mm in spring and summer. Once the surface of a soil becomes dry water will continue to be lost but much more slowly. After about a week, the rate may fall to about a tenth of the original value. The loss is then influenced by the rate of transfer of water upwards from moist soil below. As long as soil remains bare the total loss of water remains small, even after long periods without rain. For example, in a very sandy soil which by its nature contains only a small amount of water the total loss after a month's drought may be only about 15 mm, and for a clayey soil the total loss may be up to 30 mm. Figure 6.1 shows that for the Midlands of England, bare soil would dry out to a maximum deficit of less than 25 mm, compared to 120 mm under winter wheat in the same season. Whenever moist soil is brought up to the surface by cultivation the rate of water loss is increased again, close to the original rate for a wet soil surface.

Water loss during early growth

Once leaves appear above ground, whether of weed or crop, water is taken from the soil by roots and lost through the leaves by transpiration. The total water loss is then the sum of direct evaporation from the soil surface plus transpiration (i.e. 'evaporation' through stomata from the inner surfaces of leaves). The amount of water transpired depends amongst other factors on the area of the leaf surfaces. While the plants remain small after emergence, water losses by transpiration are small. As the plants grow and leaf area increases so the water loss through the leaves increases. Once a field begins to look 'green' then water losses from the soil are almost wholly due to transpiration.

Water use by the crop

Unlike nutrients, water does not accumulate within the plant but evaporates and is lost. This loss creates a water deficit within the leaf; a water tension develops which is transmitted via the veins in the leaf down the stem to the roots thereby enabling them to take in water from the soil. In the vicinity of a root, the soil dries, also creating a local increase in water tension and water transfer then takes place from wetter to drier soil (i.e. towards the root).

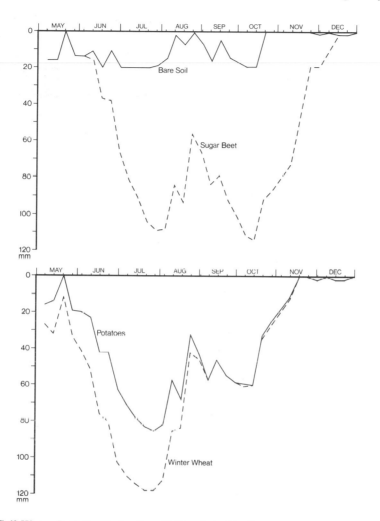

FIGURE 6.1 Soil Water Deficits Under Bare Soil and Arable Crops.

The figures are for the West Midlands of England in a typical season (1986). They show that bare soil never dried out more than 20 mm at any time during the summer and by mid October had rewetted to field capacity. Sugar beet and potatoes dried the land at the same rate as bare soil prior to emergence and then each extracted water at a faster rate until a wet spell in August partially rewetted the soil. Sugar beet extracted water for transpiration in autumn as long as growth continued. Winter wheat, coming through winter with a full leaf cover, dried the soil earlier in spring than either of the root crops and extracted a greater amount of water, reaching a peak deficit of about 120 mm; the rate was reduced once the crop began to ripen.

(Based on MORECS data with permission from the Meteorological Office)

Within the normal range of agricultural crops the quantity of water required for transpiration does not depend so much on the type of plant as on the length of time the land is covered with leaves. In early growth it depends on the leaf area but as soon as there is a complete canopy of leaves the amount is governed by atmospheric factors. Sunshine, wind speed, temperature and relative humidity are involved and their effects are almost independent of the type of crop or soil unless the soil is dry enough to stress the crop. However, because there are differences in the dates that crops emerge, reach full ground cover and reach maturity, the rate of soil drying is influenced by the type of crop as shown in Figure 6.1. This compares losses of water from bare soil, and a number of crops in the Midlands of England.

In temperate climates there is rarely enough rainfall during the growing season to meet the plants' demand for water and a shortfall, or soil water deficit, develops and increases as the season progresses. The peak of dryness usually occurs towards the end of summer, depending on the type of crop as shown in Figure 6.1. Later in the year rainfall exceeds transpiration and soil gradually rewets until it is fully recharged to field capacity.

The magnitude of the peak water deficit (i.e. when the soil is at its driest) is one of the most important climatic characteristics of any area, because it can determine whether or not irrigation may be worthwhile. If soil characteristics are such that soil water reserves are exhausted before the driest part of the year, then the transpiration rate will fall. Therefore the peak deficit values are expressed in terms of potential soil water deficits, that is, the values that would be reached where there was ample water in the soil. Figure 6.2 shows average maximum values for mainland Britain. In drier than average years, larger values will occur. In conditions of severe drought, archaeologists are able to use crop marks to locate ancient foundations because of the effects these have on soil depth and thus on access to available water by the crops.

There are many reasons why the data in Figure 6.2 should be examined carefully and their significance understood. On an individual farm the average peak value should be known, as this plays an important part in assessing the quality of the land, the

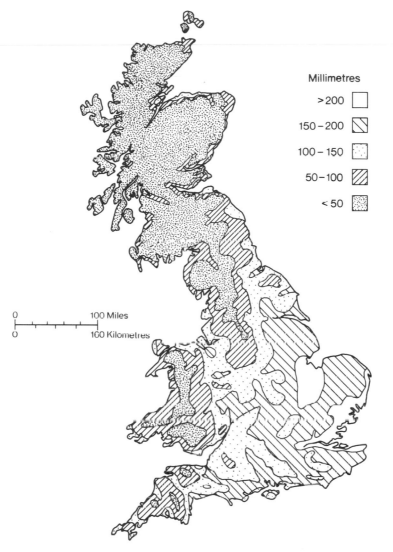

Millimetres

> 200

150 – 200

100 – 150

50 – 100

< 50

0   100 Miles

0   100 Kilometres

FIGURE 6.2 *Average Maximum Potential Soil Water Deficits*

In practical terms, this means the maximum dryness that the soil reaches in summer under grass, or other leafy crop with a continuous cover, grown without irrigation in a soil which contains enough water to permit unrestricted growth.

(Based on Meteorological Office data, and compiled from publications of the Soil Survey of England and Wales and of the Soil Survey of Scotland) soil depth required to satisfy peak crop water demands, the depth to which soil examination should extend to check on root developoment and the need for field drainage. Figure 6.2 is also useful for comparing different areas of the country and for example whether farming practices or the results of field research in one area are applicable to another. Many Research Institutes concerned with soils and field crops in England are in parts of the country with average maximum soil water deficits of around 180 mm. Care must be taken to examine the relevance of the results of field experiments done at these Institutes to less dry parts of the country.

To illustrate the use of 'the average maximum potential soil water deficit', two examples will be given. In parts of the north east of Scotland very hard layers of soil are commonly found under much of the arable land at a shallow depth of 35 − 40 cm; these 'indurated' layers were formed during periglacial periods of the last Ice Age and are so dense that they do not permit roots to grow any further into the soil. However, crop growth and yields are unaffected except in drought years. The reason for the lack of significance of this condition lies in the fact that because of cool moist summers the soil water deficit is, on average, no greater than 70 mm. This amount of water can be obtained readily from the limited depth of soil available. A similar soil found in warmer and drier areas of the south east of England where the average soil water deficit was 180 mm, would be useless for arable cropping unless irrigation were available.

Crop type and soil water use

Crops which grow continuously throughout the spring and summer months will have the greatest demand for water. The most 'greedy' consumer of water is therefore grass as it has full cover in spring and growth continues uninterrupted right through the summer until low light intensity and low temperatures bring the growing season to an end. Sugar beet, forage turnips and kale also grow through the late summer and early autumn, but have a lower water consumption in spring as there is less water lost from the bare seedbed and while the plant leaf cover is low. The differences in water extraction between a number of crops is shown in Figure 6.1.

Water use for cereals depends upon whether they are autumn or spring sown. Autumn sown crops come through the winter with a substantial leaf cover over the ground and water extraction from the soil in spring is therefore similar to grass. With spring sown crops, however, there are several weeks when the soil is bare or partially covered by crop, so that water use is less than for an overwintered crop. When cereals begin to ripen transpiration declines so that by the time a ripe crop is harvested, it has virtually ceased. Any rain falling just before harvest enters the soil (apart from a small amount held in the crop) and reduces the soil water deficit.

Potatoes do not consume water for transpiration until they have emerged, and soil water deficits at the end of May would normally be less than, say, under spring barley. With potatoes, water loss is complicated by the practice of inter-row cultivation which brings moist soil to the surface, thereby increasing the water lost by direct evaporation. In late summer potatoes transpire water only as long as green leaf cover is maintained, and the rate would decline as senescence or blight reduce leaf cover. When potato haulms are burnt off, transpiration ceases, and there is no further drying of the soil other than a small loss by evaporation from the surface. The risk of having wet soil conditions at harvest is increased by the use of irrigation because this aims to reduce peak soil water deficits to a maximum of 30 – 35 mm, and this amount of rain would be all that was required for the land to reach field capacity.

Water loss from undisturbed fallow land is low, provided it is kept free of transpiring weeds. The significance is that it will take comparatively little rain to recharge the soil to field capacity and the land can consequently be quite wet under fallow in late summer or autumn with a risk of soil damage by cultivation. Exactly the same occurs in any patches of crop failure or on uncropped headlands: land without the drying effect of transpiration through plants will lie much wetter with a distinct risk of serious compaction to the soil by tractors, harvesters or trailers which may have to cross such a bare area.

Chapter 7

SOIL COLOUR AND SOIL AERATION

The colour of a soil provides much evidence of value in soil husbandry. Part of the colour is derived from the primary rock particles which make up the soil, but much is due to changes which have taken place since the soil was formed. These changes include loss by solution, the removal or transfer of particles, and the alteration of the original minerals. In many soils the dominant colour of the particles is due to the presence of iron-containing minerals in the original rocks which have weathered to their predominantly red, brown or reddish-brown forms. Once vegetation has become established, other changes in colour are then due to the addition and transfer of organic materials. Still further changes are the result of the exclusion of oxygen from the soil and the development of anaerobic conditions. The period taken for changes in colour to occur may range from a few hours to many centuries.

The alterations in colour which take place are also affected by the chemical composition of the soil and by the position of the soil in the landscape, by the climate, by the type of vegetation and biotic life in the soil. Man too has an important role by his use and management of the soil.

Scientists make great use of soil colour patterns in studying the development of soils, and those seeking more information on this aspect are referred to appropriate books listed in Appendix 1. The aspects of soil colour covered in this chapter are confined to those of most significance from a practical viewpoint in soil husbandry and management: organic matter, aeration and drainage.

Effects of Organic Matter

The original green, yellow or white colours of plant material soon darken to various shades of brown when left on the surface or when they are incorporated into the soil, and all shape and structure of the original plant material is eventually lost. Most organic matter added to the soil is decomposed by microorganisms, and a proportion of this processed material is resistant to further decay, and is termed soil humus. The colour that humus adds to the soil depends on the physical and chemical environment. In much of lowland Britain, humus darkens the soil, masking the colour of the original minerals to give a brown uniformly coloured layer on the surface, usually to a depth of 15 – 20 cm. This depth may be increased by ploughing or cultivation, the action of which may mix the surface layer to the depth of working. The colour of a soil is also affected by the concentration of humus present, and as the content increases the soil darkens. Soils which contain a high amount of humus are dark brown, almost black in colour. Slow decomposition of organic matter and the accumulation of humus to give a dark coloured soil may be caused by waterlogging, by low soil temperatures and by strongly acid conditions.

Soil Aeration: changes induced when the oxygen supply is inadequate.

Oxygen is essential for the respiration of roots, and for the majority of organisms which inhabit the soil. In soils where the supply of oxygen, either in the soil air or dissolved in water, cannot meet the demand for respiration, those organisms which are obliged to use oxygen cease to function. However, there are also microorganisms in soils which can continue to thrive when the oxygen supply drops, and there are others which flourish only when oxygen is very low or absent. In soils without oxygen (anaerobic conditions) many changes are induced which because of their significance, will be described in detail. The changes which take place once a soil becomes devoid of oxygen occur in a fixed sequence as long as oxygen remains absent; however, some changes overlap and because of the varied conditions often found within a soil, several may be going on at the same time. The sequence of changes which takes place is described below, stage by stage. The effects of the different processes are further complicated by the fact that some steps are reversible, others are not.

A. Oxygen present, prior to or after saturation: aerobic decomposition of organic matter, with the main product being carbon dioxide; nitrogen in organic matter released as ammonium and converted to nitrate ions

B. Saturation stage 1: Oxygen concentration falls to zero, loss by microbial action of nitrate to nitrite, oxides of nitrogen and nitrogen gas, no associated changes in colour

stage 2: Reduction of manganese and iron compounds from insoluble to more soluble forms which can move to new locations, iron in the soluble ferrous form may be seen as greyish, bluish or greenish colours; many of these changes are reversible (discussed below)

stage 3: Reduction of sulphate to sulphide which may give rise to a characteristic sulphidic smell
N.B. Hydrogen sulphide is highly toxic and in a deep soil pit when this gas may be present, great care should be taken to avoid breathing it.

stage 4: Organic materials may decompose to produce a large number of organic acids and hydrocarbons.
(Note: the expression 'reduction' is a chemical term which refers to the opposite process to oxidation, it does not simply mean a smaller value).

Several of the products of anaerobic conditions may have adverse effects on plants. These products include ferrous ions, nitrite, sulphides, organic acids such as acetic acid, and hydrocarbons such as ethylene.

Changes following the re-entry of air into an anaerobic soil

When air re-enters a soil the colours do not necessarily revert to those formerly present. Iron and manganese are mobile in their reduced form; they may be washed down the soil profile or they may move into aggregates, the centres of which may still be aerated. As a result of the transfer processes, some areas of the soil may lose iron and manganese, others may gain. The losses of manganese may not be discernible, but when iron is removed, grey colours are usually left behind. These changes are often seen in clayey soils as grey-lined cracks penetrating deeply into the soil; such changes are permanent and would be visible whether the soil was saturated and anaerobic, or dry and aerated at the time of inspection. In clayey soils, some of the iron and manganese may move sideways into aggregates when mobile and oxidise to form pea-sized nodules which may be rust coloured or almost black. Where air enters a crack or hole made by a root or earthworm which passes into a saturated and reduced soil, oxidation of ferrous to ferric forms of iron occurs in close proximity and a sharp contrast in colour may be seen as a bright rusty ring of ferric enriched soil. Some cementing of the soil particles with this form of iron may also occur so that a crisp hard pipe is seen around the location of oxygen entry.

Care and skill is needed to distinguish between grey streaks or tongues where iron has been removed from soil by successive periods of reduction in times past, and those greyish or bluish hues due to the current prescence of iron in its ferrous form. Where confirmation is necessary, simple tests for the presence of ferrous ions may be made by specialist advisers.

The foregoing section describes the changes in colour where saturation by water is the primary cause of oxygen depletion. Compaction of soil can also reduce the supply of oxygen entering the soil and induce anaerobic pockets in topsoils, typically under wheel tracks and hoof prints.

It is important to appreciate that while the complex processes of reduction in soils may be the result of microbial action in anaerobic conditions, the changes in colour due to re-oxidation are predominantly chemical in nature. Any factor which influences the oxygen demand within a soil (as well as those affecting the supply of oxygen) therefore strongly affects the likelihood or duration of reducing conditions. These factors include temperature and the amount and quality of organic matter as a substrate for microbial life. When turf or any crop residue such as sugar beet top is is turned in and surrounded by compressed soil it is common to find anaerobic pockets around each piece of plant debris, detectable by its grey colour and also by its malodorous sulphide smell.

In subsoils with sufficient clay to shrink when dry, roots grow mainly down the cracks and are often seen as webs on the crack face. When the cracks are open in summer, fine topsoil falls down them so that the organic content is enhanced alongside the crack by the addition of both roots and topsoil. Thus when the soil re-saturates in autumn, reduction can take place more intensely, close to the face of a crack, than at locations within the soil, which do not have this extra organic matter. The consequence is that iron is stripped from the crack faces which are commonly seen as a uniform continuous pale grey colour, whilst variegated rusty colours are visible within the structural units.

Under cool conditions, reduction proceeds very slowly, but when soils are very warm in summer or early autumn, the onset of reduction can be rapid soon after anaerobic conditions occur. If the rain is prolonged and heavy, and saturation continues for a few days, large losses of N may occur. If soil compaction is also present in the topsoil, not only will this increase the risk of saturation, but will enhance the degree of anaerobism. On the other hand saturation in winter, even if prolonged, may cause little or no reduction, because the low temperatures limit significant microbial activity in the soil.

Drainage
The colour changes which take place in subsoils as a result of repeated seasonal cycles of reduction and oxidation, are frequently used in the assessment of soil drainage status and also in field drainage design. The intensity of grey and rusty mottled colours caused by cycles of reduction and oxidation, and their proximity to the soil surface are key criteria. Colour changes are not the only diagnostic features used, and soil structure, soil texture, bulk density and the depth of the water table from the surface are also important.

When a soil is drained and waterlogging no longer occurs, any rusty coloured nodules or areas caused by an enhanced iron content will remain where they are, and any grey tongues or crack faces created by the removal of iron will also remain in place. Thus many of the red and grey tones formed during the period before the soil was drained can remain after drainage as evidence of past conditions and may not reflect the current state. Care is therefore needed in interpretation of greys and reds, and if in doubt, a ferrous iron test can be used to determine whether grey colours are past relics or due to active reduction.

When a soil is dominated by minerals which give it strong reddish colours, such as some of the red clays in the Midlands of England and in Eastern Scotland, the intensity of the red hues may mask any changes due to reduction/oxidation cycles. Therefore evidence of reduction in such soils is difficult to obtain by visual examination alone. Similar difficulties occur where both red and grey coloured minerals are present in the same soil.

Section B: SOIL HUSBANDRY
                      IN PRACTICE

The first four Chapters in this section describe a number of soil problems and discuss their solution. The examples given are not derived
from a comprehensive survey but have been chosen to illustrate those
typical of present-day agriculture. They also demonstrate the need for
careful and detailed study of the soil before reaching conclusions as to
the cause of the problem and before planning remedial work.

Each soil is unique and its properties at any time reflect in part its
inherent characteristics and in part its past use and management. Therefore the examples described may not fit exactly the conditions found on
a particular farm, but are given as illustrations for general guidance.
Before examining any problem, the climate of the locality in which it
occurs must be considered. A dry area requires a deep soil to provide
large reserves of water to enable crops to thrive in summer; in a wetter
area shallow soils may be adequate to produce good yields. Any problem must also be examined in context of the quality of the land. Some
difficulties may be so intractable that a change in cropping or land use
may be a better solution than to struggle on regardless of costs.

Problems sometimes affect a whole field though it is much more
common to see part, often a small part, affected. It is sensible to begin
by asking the simplest questions first: is the affected area of different
soil, or in a hollow, or on a crest? Is acidity involved? Has past soil
management any involvement, such as the site of a muck heap, building, track or feeding trough? Does the pattern fit some cultural treatment such as a spray or fertilizer application, either recent or residual?
Is the problem area new or has it been seen before ? Is frost or wind
damage possible?

In each example, the identification and cause of the problem is
discussed, and remedial measures are outlined. However, the actual
solution for a particular problem must be related to the specific conditions that are found. Careful methodical examination is required to
find the correct explanation for the cause of any problem and also to
monitor the success or otherwise of any remedial work done.

Chapter 8 PROBLEMS RELATED TO SOIL COMPACTION

Over the years more concern has probably been shown about over-compaction than to any other aspect of soil husbandry. Responses to subsoiling were recorded as long ago as 1852, long before the self-propelled wheeled tractor appeared. Figure 8.1 shows a horse-drawn subsoiler last used in the 1930's. The creation of over-compaction is therefore not a new problem. However, vehicles and trailers are getting heavier and pressures may be transmitted to greater depths in the soil. Farmers should therefore be alert to the possibility of a compact layer forming beneath the normal depth of cultivation and to watch out for signs of this developing.

The effects of over-compaction are often seen first as patches of weak or failed crop, often in the lower or wetter parts of a field. Many examples can be seen from the roadside on any journey in lowland Britain. They may often be linked to poor drainage too, and the separation of problems into those due to over-compaction and those due to wetness is not always possible.

Over-compaction can usually be traced to pressure applied to the soil when it was wet and soft, and the incidence is therefore greater after wet seasons, particularly when heavy rain coincides with either seedbed preparation or crop harvest. Factual evidence on the incidence of over-compaction was obtained in a postal survey conducted in Scotland by the Scottish Institute of Agricultural Engineering, published as Research Summary No. 3 in 1987. The results showed that 25% of farmers considered that over-compaction problems occurred either every year or in most years; only 13% never encountered them. While most farmers (58%) did not consider that compaction problems had become more prevalent during the last five years (1979 – 1984),

FIGURE 8.1 Examples of Subsoilers — Old and New.

These implements are used for breaking over-compact layers of soil which lie beneath the depth of normal tillage:

    (Above) A horse-drawn subsoiler last used in the 1930's

    (Below) A triple stem unit pulled by a powerful tractor.

20% thought that there had been an increase. Machine operations considered most damaging were harvesting of potatoes and root crops, and the spreading of dung and slurry. Spraying, grain harvesting, seedbed cultivations, lime spreading and silage making also caused problems. In this survey, the majority of farmers (82%) reported that they took precautions to overcome over-compaction by deeper ploughing or subsoiling, the use of reduced ground pressure under vehicles, avoidance of traffic on wet soils and by limiting traffic to tramlines.

The effects of over-compaction on crop yields are less clear. Certainly crop failure or severe reductions in yield can occur, usually confined to a small part of an affected field. In the Scottish survey, crops considered to be most affected by compaction were oilseed rape, peas, beans and other vegetables; among cereal growers, half considered that their crops showed small yield depressions due to compaction.

One of the factors influencing the effect that over-compaction may have on crop development and yield is the weather and in particular the dryness of the season. If roots are restricted in their downward growth by compact soil, then crop stress due to inadequate access to soil water reserves may cause a yield depression. In a season with adequate rain, the same restriction in root depth may have an insignificant influence on crop growth.

Not all effects of over-compaction are due to the mechanical restriction of roots. Drainage may be affected by the slowing down of water moving through the compact layer. In some cases this may lead to saturation of the soil by water, the onset of anaerobic conditions and the loss of nitrogen by denitrification. In other cases, a layer of soft soil forms above the compact layer, leading to traction difficulties and further damage to the soil.

It should not be necessary to wait for a wet summer or a very dry summer to show up problems of over-compaction; regular examination of the soil should be established as a routine operation. If this technique is followed, then remedial action can be planned and executed under soil conditions when effective treatment can be applied. When problems show up in a wet season the chances of finding suitable remedies are much reduced.

FIGURE 8.2 The Importance of Post-harvest Tillage (ii).
Unrelieved compaction leading to water standing on the surface in patches is a common sight in autumn in all parts of the country.

Deep cultivation (i.e. subsoiling), is practised by some farmers as a routine operation but is this 'insurance' justified? Certainly where there is evidence that compaction is present and restricting the permeability of the soil, the benefits should be worthwhile. As a regular routine in other soils there is little or no evidence of any benefit, indeed harm may result.

Looking for soil compaction

In order to determine whether significant compaction is present, several holes should be dug, preferably by mechanical digger to display a section of soil. Compaction may be found on the surface of the land, within the depth of ploughing or cultivation and just below the working depth of ploughs where the share scrapes across the soil and the open furrow receives the pressure from the tyres of wheeled tractors. Further details on how to examine soils for compact layers are given in Chapter 14.

At the boundary between the tilled soil and the undisturbed soil beneath, there is almost always a distinct contrast in soil structure, from the loosened often granular cultivated tilth to a firm more compact base. This difference must not be mistaken for 'compaction' though the lower layer may be much more dense than that above. Examination of the soil in April or May may provide direct evidence from the distribution of crop roots on whether or not the boundary has affected root penetration. In late summer when the soil is at its driest and hardest it is difficult to distinguish between a naturally dry but hard subsoil and one which has been compacted by mechanical pressure. The evidence requires to be reviewed by considering the uniformity and performance of the crop itself. If growth of the crop was even and has produced a satisfactory yield then man-made compaction, even if present, may not have had a significant effect.

Signs that over-compaction at the base of cultivation depth is present, commonly called a soil pan could show up in a soil pit as one or more of the following:

● roots checked at the upper boundary of the soil pan with some growing horizontally and with few or none below;

● water held up after heavy rain, oozing out of the side of the pit just above the soil pan;

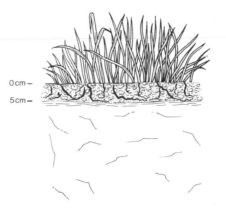

0 cm —
5 cm —

FIGURE 8.3 *Effect of Shallow Compaction on the Growth and Composition of Grass.*

(Upper sketch) Excessive cultivation of damp soil (fine sandy loam) caused over-compaction at 5 cm, which led to shallow root development, stunted and pale growth of grass deficient in N and K. The poor growth of the sward was due to water stress because of rapid drying out of the upper 5 cm of soil, and to multiple nutrient deficiencies induced not by shortages in the soil but by severely reduced uptake from the dry soil.

(Lower sketch) Normal crop on the same field, where the soil was drier when cultivated, showing no restriction of rooting and vigorous growth of herbage.

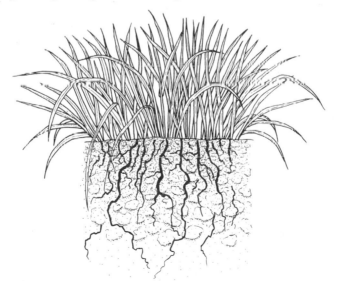

● pockets of grey anaerobic soil within the topsoil or just below it, within the compact soil;

● when examined in spring or early summer, a dry topsoil and a sharp change to a much moister subsoil may be indicative of the absence of roots to extract water from the subsoil. Conversely, if a uniform profile of moisture was found in spring and roots were growing well down into the soil, then it is unlikely that significant compaction was present. Some of these points are illustrated in Figure 8.3.

Subsoiling

To deal with compaction found below the depth of normal tillage machinery a subsoiler is required. Treatment is expensive in terms of power, fuel and labour, and should be reserved for those areas, possibly only parts of a field, for which the evidence justifies its use. When a positive decision has been made to break up the subsoil, the depth and interval between tines should be chosen after examining the effects of a test run. If done blind without any examination of the need or effects, the effort may be wasted. When compact soil is broken up the volume increases, usually seen as an upward displacement of the surface; a rise of 10 – 20 cm may be expected. This can produce a ridged or rippled effect if the interval between passes is too wide. If done correctly, the subsoiled land should be almost level.

Subsoiling can also affect drainage because of increased permeability along the tine channel, particularly at its base. This zone may bear the imprint of the tine and thus subsoiling has sometimes been referred to as 'square moling'. On slow draining clays, it is necessary to ensure that if water runs into the subsoil channel, it can find an exit into a drain. If it cannot, water may accumulate as a wet layer in the subsoil, or run down to flood low areas of the field.

The timing of subsoiling is important in relation to the water content of the soil. To be effective, the soil must be dry enough to shatter, at the depth where fracturing and loosening is required. If too soft, the subsoil tine will cut a slot through the soil but no lateral cracking would take place. In wet seasons, it may be necessary to break through a compact layer whilst it is still wet to allow water to drain through, and to regard such

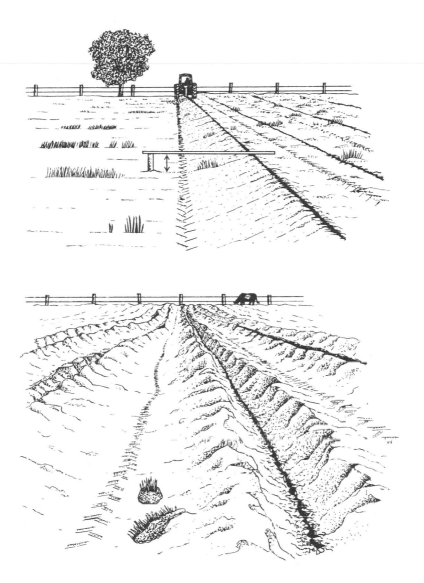

FIGURE 8.4 *Effect of Subsoil Loosening on the Land Surface.*

In both examples, the surface has been displaced upwards to accommodate the loosening effect. The upper sketch shows an even uplift of the land subsoiled, with a distinct slope between loosened and unloosened land; the lower sketch also shows the loosening effect but only directly along the tine track, with undisturbed land between.

treatment as a temporary measure. Comprehensive shattering of a compact layer will have to wait for drier conditions for it to be effective. Because of the difficulty of dealing with compaction in wet seasons, it is better to make regular checks of soils under normal conditions so that any potential problems can be dealt with effectively before they become serious.

Tramlines and wheeltracks

The technique of using the same wheeltracks for successive applications of chemicals over the season is a well established practice for cereals and other arable crops. The timing of an application is determined by the presence of pest, disease or nutrient shortage, and also by the stage of growth of the crop. This means that ground may be wet and soft when run on, so that tracks may become deeper as the season progresses.

The objective of using 'tramlines' is to provide an easy-to-see location for the even application of chemicals and to restrict the unavoidable compaction of the soil to only a few per cent of the land area. However, sinkage may be considerable and it is not uncommon to find tracks 30 cm or more deep on softer parts of a field. The incised tracks can be filled readily by cross cultivation after harvest but much of the dense soil, which may extend to 60 cm or deeper, may be well below the depth of cultivation. It is therefore advisable to break up compaction before it becomes excessively deep, but this can be done only when the soil is dry — a difficult criterion to meet particularly in low ground where compaction is likely to be greatest. Water infiltration under tracks is often very restricted and a common feature is to see tracks water-filled in lower parts of a field even to the brim. Wet hollows can be the ultimate result. Erosion may also occur on steeper ground. Some reduction of the problem of wet hollows may occur if tracks run across, rather than up and down a slope. Where wet soft areas are already present, tramlines may make them worse, and skilful drainage may be needed to dry them out. Where tracks are known to cause problems due to reduced penetration of water, loosening of the compact soil with a single tine after the initial pass may improve the permeability of the track and render it firmer for subsequent passes. If recompaction occurs this treatment may need to be repeated.

Figure 8.5 Fracturing of Compact Soil Under Tramlines.

Tramline compaction fractured after harvest and a hole dug to check that all the dense soil had been loosened.

Harvest tracks

Under the mental strains of harvest, it is a great temptation to press ahead with combining or lifting and to leave behind any damaged soil to deal with at a later and more convenient time. However, it is clear from field experience that any delay in treating the soil brings additional problems. Tracks, whether originating from harvester, loaded trailers or the tractors that pull them, are unavoidable and under each, soil compaction of varying intensity is the result with a corresponding reduction in the infiltration rate of water. One obvious result is that subsequent rain is slow to drain from these tracks and may collect in them or run down slopes to low ground. If this occurs land work, even harvest on the rest of the field, may be delayed or become impossible. It is therefore very important to break up compaction under harvest tracks without delay, so that any subsequent rain can drain through. If rain is forecast this may mean cultivation on the same day, particularly on headlands and near field exits where the frequency of tracks is greater. This should be done even if only part of the field has been harvested, otherwise later tracking may be done under wet slippery surface conditions leading to further and possibly greater damage. The depth of cultivation to break up tracks should be chosen by examining the soil; it may be quite shallow, to leave a porous but firm surface. The direction of the initial cultivation should cross dominant tracks and run partially across slopes, so that water moving over the surface may be intercepted and drain into the soil.

Poaching of pastures

Poaching is a persistent and widespread problem in wetter areas of Britain and in wet seasons elsewhere. Investigations by the Animal and Grassland Research Institute have lead to the publication of a map showing the location of land classed as having a low, variable or high susceptibility to poaching; over 3 million ha. of land in England and Wales was classified as highly susceptible. The incidence of poaching is related to rainfall, soil properties and grazing intensity. It occurs when a soil is so soft that the hooves of grazing animals cannot be supported on the surface and they press into the soil to leave depressions up to 10 cm or more deep. It is common to find hoof imprints water-filled and distinct grey anaerobic zones of soil may be seen beneath them. With regular poaching a compact layer of soil may develop some 7 − 12 cm below the surface, and this may form an almost continuous layer of grey anaerobic soil. Once it has

FIGURE 8.6 *The Importance of Post-harvest Tillage (iii).*

Tillage across wheel ruts done soon after lifting potatoes allowed subsequent rain to drain into the land, leaving the surface dry and without surface ponding.

formed, a poached soil tends to be self-perpetuating as the compaction reduces permeability and increases the risk of further damage. The yield from a poached pasture will be much reduced both because of direct damage to the plant, and also because of lack of aeration in the soil inhibiting root growth and causing a reduction in the amount of nitrogen available in forms suitable for crop use. Poached pastures are often pale green or yellow in colour whether or not nitrogen fertilizer has been applied.

Poaching leaves behind a damaged sward, an uneven surface and a compact soil. There seems to be no generally applicable technique to alleviate the damage and restore the land to its former capability. The soil damage can persist over winter so that a pasture that is poached one summer can be found with a wet soft surface the following spring, susceptible to yet more damage.

The surface roughness left by poaching may be reduced by a heavy roller, but this does not provide any improvement to the condition of the soil below. Increased permeability to soil and water is required to effect an improvement but under pasture this is difficult to achieve. To give a general statement advocating subsoiling is an inadequate response. Grassland is found mainly in the wetter and cooler parts of the country and when poached, soils lie wet for long periods making any land work difficult. The soils are therefore seldom dry enough for subsoiling to be effective. The prime need is to encourage surface water to drain through the soil, to prevent further damage. Careful examination of the soil is required to locate the depth and thickness of any offending layer which may be not far below the surface, possibly 12 − 18 cm. Shallow subsoiling or moling with a smaller version of the traditional mole plough may be effective as an initial step, with the depth controlled to get just below the compaction and no more, so that the dense layer is partially loosened, even if done in wet conditions. The subsoiler may be little more than a modified cultivator and a narrow tine may reduce sward damage and uplift, with a leading disc to prevent the sod tearing and upturning. A slant-leg subsoiler may also be used, and operated slightly deeper to prevent detachment of the turf. A certain amount of damage to the sward is inevitable, but this should be temporary, though if the degree of heave is distinct,

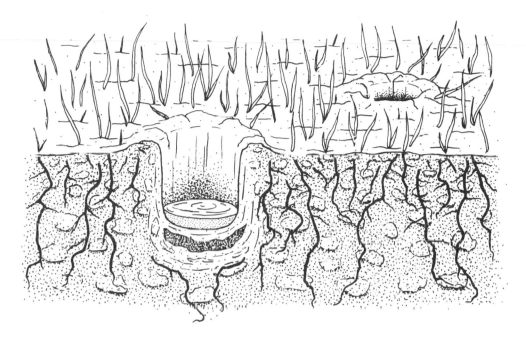

FIGURE 8.7 *Effects of Poaching of Grassland on Soil Properties.*

Poaching of wet pastures can be just as damaging to the soil as the use of heavy machinery. The permeability of the soil to water and air beneath hoof imprints is reduced, and grey anaerobic zones may be found which, if the poaching is severe or prolonged, may coalesce to form a continuous layer.

an undulating surface may result. For land to be grazed this may not be a hazard.

It must be stressed that the shallow treatment described above is to deal with the direct effects of poaching. It has been assumed that once the slots are cut through the dense layer the water can drain away below. If the land as a whole is poorly drained then shallow subsoiling could be ineffective or bring about only temporary relief.

To produce a consistent and satisfactory output from grassland requires effective field drainage, unless the soil drains well naturally. A soundly designed system, correctly installed and regularly maintained, is a key requirement and can do much to prevent the onset of poaching problems.

Land which is severely poached must be reseeded to restore production. Cultivation for the preparation of a seedbed would normally be deep enough to loosen compact soil created by poaching. In cases where the poaching has created deep regular troughs, then deep land work is needed. Soil examination to locate the maximum depth of compaction and to plan remedial cultivation is required if improvements are to be effective. On severely, or even moderately, poached land light cultivation of the surface to prepare a shallow seedbed can not be recommended as the damaged compact soil may remain untouched below and surface wetness would recur. Nor can direct drilling of poached land be recommended for the same reason.

In wetter areas and on slow draining clays, the point must be made that intensive grazing systems may not be viable in the long term. If high output is demanded then provision should be made to house stock for a longer winter period, and also to bring them in at any time when wet weather renders the soil too soft to be grazed without marked poaching. On some farms it may be possible to avoid overall poaching by preparing and reserving some land specifically for use in wet weather. This may be fields or parts of fields which can be fenced off, that are naturally dry or intensively drained, or those about to be reseeded so that any damage is of less consequence.

Chapter 9 PROBLEMS OF SOIL STRUCTURE

This chapter gives examples of some commonly found problems. A full discussion on the development and deterioration of soil structure is given in Chapter 4.

Surface Capping

This problem occurs when a surface tilth disintegrates and a slurry-like layer forms. A typical situation would be when a finely aggregated soil is exposed to heavy or prolonged rain. The energy of raindrops is dissipated on impact with the soil and the initial result is to disrupt the surface of aggregates. If the rain continues the external layer of the aggregates is washed off exposing inner material; in heavy or prolonged storms the degradation may eventually destroy every aggregate so that a continuous skin is formed on the surface of the land. A similar condition can result from the rapid wetting of aggregates when air entrapped within forces its way to the surface and breaks them apart. The two agents, rain batter and rapid wetting, act simultaneously when heavy rain is prolonged. The finer particles of clay and silt detached from aggregates move a short distance into the soil, blocking the pores so that infiltration of both air and water is reduced. The consequence is that emergence may be prevented and the growth of seedlings stopped due to lack of oxygen while the layer remains wet. On drying the surface skin can harden to form a rigid cap which may be strong enough to prevent seedlings breaking through.

This phenomenon is restricted to a narrow range of soils — those with a high content of fine sand and very fine sand and to a lesser extent, silty soils. On susceptible soils the following practical measures can be taken to decrease the risk of capping:-

● retain previous crop residues on the surface as a protective cover;

● do not plough or till deeper than necessary, so that crop residues are retained near the surface;

● avoid excessive tillage, particularly with powered cultivators if this produces a very fine seedbed;

● reduce the length of time that a fine seedbed is exposed to rain;

● improve the stability of surface aggregates by any action which will increase the soil organic matter concentration near the surface.

Most severe problems have been seen when heavy rain falls onto a fine seedbed within a few days of sowing onions, swedes and sugar beet; erratic germination was the result and many plants never emerged. If a cap forms more than 2 cm thick, cereals too may not emerge, but delay in emergence, rather than death of seedlings is more usual. In some instances re-sowing is required, though more often variable emergence and a variable crop of reduced quality is the result of capping.

If a cap forms prior to drilling, light harrowing or rolling when the surface is dry would normally be enough to crush the cap and recreate a seedbed. When a cap forms after sowing, any cultivation has to wait until the surface is dry, by which time the seedlings may well have germinated beneath the cap and would be very sensitive to any pressure applied directly above. However, shallow inter-row cultivation may displace or fracture a cap where crops are grown in rows wide enough for this to be done. If the problem is severe and persistent, transplanted crops can be grown which by-pass the need for seedlings to emerge through a capped surface.

Stability of aggregates on the surface of the soil may be temporarily improved by the use of proprietary organic polymers which may be applied to a newly prepared seedbed to cover either the whole surface or to a band above the seed,

Slumping and hard setting

After cultivation, all soils experience a degree of settling. However some soils with very unstable aggregates may slump

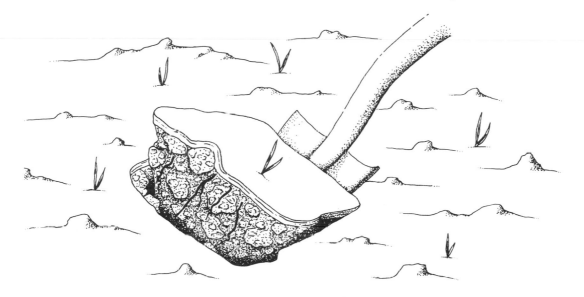

FIGURE 9.1 Disintegration of Surface Structure

When large raindrops hit bare soil, their energy may break apart the aggregates, to form a skin on the surface; this phenomenon occurs almost wholly in soils which contain a high proportion of very fine sand or silt sized particles. Such a cap will reduce the permeability of the surface to water and to air, and on drying may form a continuous hard crust, shown above. Sometimes this may fracture naturally, if thick enough it may prevent the emergence of seedlings.

back after ploughing and cultivation to the same density as they had before. This condition can be followed by hard-setting where the slumped soil which has run together in the wet state dries as one complete mass without any cracks. Where this phenomenon is serious, it is difficult to prepare a good seedbed and crop development, especially in the early stages, can be held back by slow root growth. This problem is one stage worse than surface capping and occurs on soils of similar texture. It is usually associated with a soil management system which has run down the level of soil organic matter too far by intensive cropping and a low input of crop residues.

Practical measures to reduce the severity of hard-setting include:-

● avoid disturbing the soil any more than is necessary, especially when it is wet, by minimizing the number of cultivations;

● over a longer period, measures to build up the concentration of organic matter near the surface by retaining crop residues, adding manures or green manuring;

● altering rotations to give a higher proportion of crops requiring little tillage.

Underconsolidation   Despite the general concern in relation to over-compaction, lack of surface consolidation can occur in sandy soils and on peats. The effects may be seen as difficulty in achieving a correct and even depth of drilling for cereals and other crops. Subsequent growth may be weak and erratic because roots do not make good contact with the soil and fail to anchor the plants adequately. This problem is usually at its most severe in seedbeds prepared in spring after frosty weather. It can also occur in established crops which can be damaged by the heaving effect of frost, to give a soil with a loose puffy condition.

Obviously there must be a compromise between over- and underconsolidation and a sensible approach is required. If several cultivations are to be done, they can be carefully planned so that if double wheels are used on tractors, by the time of

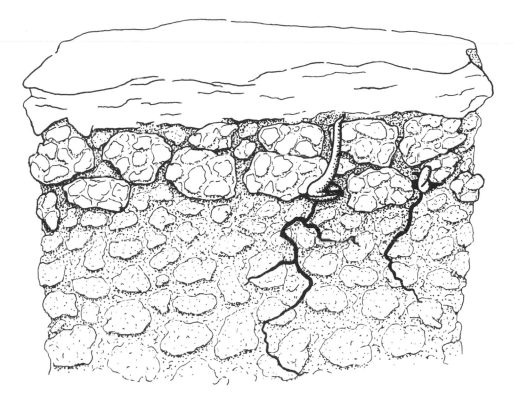

FIGURE 9.2 A Soil Cap Prevented the Emergence of Wheat.

The wheat had been sown in November into a fine seedbed, and subsequent heavy rain brought about a collapse of the surface structure. A hard cap 1 – 2 cm thick was strong enough to prevent the seedlings growing through to reach the surface – even by the following April. The texture of the soil was very fine sandy loam.

the final cultivation, all the land will have been wheel-rolled. On loose sandy soils considerable success has been achieved by the reintroduction of the furrow press attached directly to the plough to give a one-pass system, which produces an even firm surface ready for drilling.

It must be emphasised that this problem has been seen only on sands, loamy sands and peats; the degree of looseness on the surface may be assessed by foot pressure — if sinkage occurs to a depth of more than 2 − 3 cm, then additional firming may be required.

Erosion by water   Despite the fact that rainfall in the temperate maritime climate of Britain is relatively non-erosive, rarely falling faster than 25 mm per hour, minor erosion is widespread. This may be seen as narrow shallow channels, classified as rills, which can be filled in and levelled by normal cultivation. Deeper channels termed gullies also occur locally. **There is no excuse for any breach of good soil management which could cause serious erosion in Britain.**

Erosion by water is initiated when rain falls faster than the capacity of the soil to absorb it. The excess builds up, usually on the surface, though it can be beneath and, on all but level ground, it then runs down the slope. The moving water carries within it any suspended particles that have been detached by the raindrop impact. As the water gathers momentum and energy it can scour out a channel which increases in size as the water moves down the slope. The possible loss of soil is related to:

● the area of bare soil exposed to rain;

● the intensity and quantity of rainfall;

● the structure of the soil on the surface, its initial permeability and its ability to withstand the batter of rain;

● the area of land able to contribute water to an individual channel;

● the length and angle of the slope;

● the direction and type of cultivation.

FIGURE 9.3 Consolidation of Loose Soil can Improve Crop Growth
In the above example, carrots grew better where tractor wheels had compressed the sandy soil.

Although soils of all textures may erode those with a high content of fine sand and very fine sand are most at risk because of inherently weak structure. The most important predisposing factor is whether or not the soil is exposed directly to rain batter. Land totally covered with grass or crop is virtually completely protected, and so to a lesser extent is a cereal stubble because of the anchoring effect of the stems and roots. Thus land is most at risk from erosion when recently cultivated and between sowing and the development of a complete crop cover to protect the soil. For example, late sown autumn cereals leave land at risk for a long period due to slow emergence and the limited rate of growth of the crop.

Any action which reduces infiltration increases erosion risk and this is particularly noticeable in wheelings, furrows and tramlines. The risk is much increased when wheeltracks run up and down a slope, and the longer and steeper the slope, the greater the risk of erosion. To reduce the risk, infiltration along wheel tracks may be increased by running a tine through to break up the compact soil. If the direction can be changed to align tracks across a slope, or at an angle partly across, the risk from erosion would be reduced. If erosion takes place regularly the direction of all cultivations should cross the slope; in severe cases, cropping may need to be altered to give more protection to the land surface. For this purpose, grass or woodland gives almost complete protection.

Water emanating from farm roads can be a significant cause of erosion. Adequate drains and culverts must be provided and kept clear. Similarly, field headlands and tracks can be a source of eroding water if they run with the slope; if erosion occurs consideration should be given to replanning their direction and to tilling them to improve permeability.

When land erodes, the burden of soil carried in the water settles out as the speed of the water declines. This is usually at the base of the slope, in a ditch or occasionally on a public road. This transfer incurs cost and inconvenience both on the land eroded and from the soil deposited.

FIGURE 9.4 Erosion in Wheeltracks.

Water scouring down wheeltracks and tramlines is a common cause of erosion even on gently sloping land.

Erosion by wind

Soil that is capable of being eroded by wind is restricted to peats and sands, though in the north some loamy soils may generate dust clouds. The conditions required for wind erosion are unsheltered land exposed to a strong wind, with a dry bare loose surface. A wet soil is suffciently cohesive to be able to resist movement by wind so that erosion in autumn or winter is rare. Land is most at risk in spring, after crops have been sown but have not grown large enough to provide adequate protection. The loss when land blows is not only the direct loss of seed, chemicals and soil, redrilling costs and loss of yield due to delayed establishment but also the indirect cost of filled ditches, blocked roads and the nuisance, inconvenience and even danger due to clouds of dust reducing vision. Eroding sand has a considerable abrasive effect which can damage plants within and beyond the land affected. It is not only farmland that is affected, many coastal dunes and some inland heaths are regularly eroded by wind.

Soils prone to wind erosion are readily identified and control measures include:

For sand: stabilisation of the surface after sowing with proprietary resins or plastics.

For sands and peats: the sowing of a nurse crop such as barley early in spring before the season of risk; the crop of sugar beet or vegetables is then sown through the cover crop which is later killed by spraying before competition would reduce the yield of the crop. Alternatively, a narrow swath of straw may be 'planted' at intervals across the field with a machine specifically designed for this task.

In the past clay was spread on both peats and sands to improve the stability of the surface. Hedges and trees reduce windspeeds across the land, though their influence is limited to a distance about $10 - 15$ times their height.

Land use can be an important control measure on susceptible soils: land in grass or forest is fully protected from erosion by wind or water; land growing cereals is at a moderate risk of water erosion, but at less risk of wind erosion; land most at risk is that growing root and vegetable crops which are sown late in spring.

Chapter 10   PROBLEMS OF WET SOILS

Field drainage is an important technique of soil husbandry needed on about 60% of lowland Britain. This chapter does not deal with fundamental aspects concerning the design or installation of field drainage. Instead a number of practical observations are made concerning the objectives of drainage, the techniques of installation and the need for maintenance, as part of good soil husbandry.

Objectives

When land is drained, a farmer is buying time and security: time, by increasing the period of the year when landwork or grazing can be done without soil damage; and security by knowing the land can accept heavy rain so that interference with crops or cultivation will be minimal. Yields may be increased, and can also be more consistent from year to year.

An effective drainage system should respond quickly to rain and begin to discharge water from the land within a day after the beginning of a wet spell. It should also stop running within a few days after the cessation of rain. **Therefore a critical part of every drainage system is the provision of a visible outfall. Without this, no regular monitoring of the success or otherwise can be made of what is an important and expensive asset.** The position of an outfall into a ditch or stream should be clearly marked with a distinctive post and the outfall should emerge through a well constructed stable headwall.

Installation of field drains

Water in soils moves downwards under the influence of gravity – down through the soil, and down a slope. A field drain should be placed to intercept this movement so that it can collect water from the land efficiently. Flow of water to the drain is resisted by soil particles, and the size and continuity of spaces between them determine the overall permeability. When water reaches the vicinity of the drain, it may flow into it to be conducted away; drains do not 'suck' water from the soil, they simply act as a 'sink' from which water can flow out of the land.

Soils are very variable in their permeability and it is this property which largely determines the spacing of drains. On soils of low permeability, mechanical aids are used to increase the flow of water through the soil — subsoiling or mole draining. These create smooth-walled channels in the soil through which water can flow, and in many soils porous gravel is required as backfill above the drain to connect the two systems. Gravity is the only driving force; the pattern of drains must be placed so that slopes can be used to their full advantage. The primary network of clay or plastic pipes should run at an angle across a slope in one direction, with the secondary moling or subsoiling done approximately at right angles to the pipes. All drains should have an even slope to an outlet, or with the slope increasing. A decrease in slope should never occur, since water flowing through the drain would slow down at the check of slope and any sediment carried in the water would be deposited and may eventually block the drain.

Subsoiling or moling should be regarded as a farm operation once the basic pattern of gravel backfilled drains has been installed, and may be repeated at varying depths and time intervals as found necessary to keep the land dry. On grassland, narrow-stem, slant-leg subsoilers or small diameter mole drainers may reduce sward uplift and damage. Gravel backfill is expensive and is not always needed, but its use is justified in many clayey soils.

Timing of drainage operations

The timing of drainage work should be planned to coincide with dry soil conditions. If done when wet, surface damage and smearing of soil around the drain may reduce the ease with which water can reach the drain. There is much in favour of draining through a crop during summer while soil is dry. The loss of crop may not be large though there may be some inconvenience to harvest of grass or cereals due to the uneven surface left behind.

**Maintenance of
field drains**

To keep a drainage system working efficiently, thorough and regular maintenance is needed. Outfalls should be checked and cleared twice a year; rodding or jetting of the pipes should be done annually. Therefore the provision of access to the drain pipes for cleaning should be included in a sound design.

**Gateways, roads
and concrete aprons**

Gateways are often neglected as far as drainage is concerned. Because of the importance of having dry firm egress for livestock and loaded trailers, a number of short, closely spaced drains, with gravel backfill closer to the surface than usual may be worthwhile, so that shallow subsoiling may be done as required to maintain a drainable surface. It is also important to ensure that water from roads and tracks is prevented from running onto land, giving rise to wet areas or erosion in the vicinity of gateways. Drainage from areas used for washing sprayers should be carefully dealt with so that there is no possibility of contaminating land or water courses.

**Spot treatment of
wet holes and patches**

A journey through many parts of Britain will show that patches of wet ground are common, often leading to failed or poor areas of crop. In some examples, the origin may be a broken drain and reconnection should cure it. The wet patches are commonly seen in low parts of a field, in dips or hollows but not invariably. The conclusion often reached is that the origin is due to poor drainage and the solution is to lead a single drain away from the centre of the poor area. However, this is in many instances a superficial conclusion and the solution applied may give only a partial cure.

Where water collects in one particular area to show up as a wet patch, the water originates from several sources: from rain falling directly on the area affected, and from rain falling on adjacent higher ground and running down the slope. In some localities, a third possibility is uprising spring water. Wet patches may appear unexpectedly on land which has never given trouble before. In many instances the original area affected is small but the condition is liable to deteriorate and the patch become larger. In all cases, an effective solution can be found only after careful examination of the soil and of any other factors involved with the formation of the wet area.

Compact soil is often associated with wet patches and may be either a cause or a consequence. Water cannot drain through, but below the compaction the soil may be well structured and capable of draining normally. The patch may have been created initially by water running down from higher ground in wheelings, tramlines or harvest tracks; the excess water, unable to drain away fast enough, caused the soil to remain soft during subsequent landwork, resulting in compaction. **Thus a sequence of gradual deterioration develops — wetness leading to compaction leading to increased compaction, wetter conditions and so on.** If such a situation has been diagnosed, the question then is how to reverse the trend.

The first step in recovery is to prevent the problem getting worse. Getting rid of surface water must be the initial stage by whatever means are appropriate such as cutting an open drain, or breaking through the compact layer if the soil is permeable below. Where soil compaction is involved deep cultivation will be ultimately required, but as this can be done effectively only when the soil is reasonably dry, the second stage is to prepare a soil drying programme. If a crop is established but is not growing well, extra N fertiliser, spread by hand if the area is small, may aid recovery. If a crop has failed, then an attempt should be made to re-sow the crop or to grow something else, but with minimal or no further cultivation otherwise more damage may occur. Seed may be broadcast by hand if other means are impractical. The objective is to dry out the soil by extracting water for transpiration through plant leaves since evaporation alone from the surface of a bare soil will not be enough to dry the soil sufficiently.

Whether the original or a different crop is grown in the wet area, consideration should be given to sacrificing crop yield in the interests of promoting soil recovery. The soil condition, that is its dryness, should be the criterion by which to judge when remedial cultivation should be done. If delay occurs, until say after harvest on the rest of the field, the damaged soil may then be wetter and less suited for land work.

Full recovery may take several seasons of tender soil care. Field drains may or may not be required to take away water from the subsoil. It may not be wise to lead a drain directly to the centre of a wet patch. At this point the structure and permeability of the soil is worst and a drain here may have less chance of success. It may be better to place drains on one or both sides of the wet area, depending on slope configuration, where soil conditions and permeability may be better.

Wet patches may be small but may extend their influence over a much larger area; they interfere with land work, carry the risk of spreading weeds and diseases and can also function as a landing ground for raiding birds such as pigeons and crows, giving them access to unaffected crops nearby. There is therefore strong motivation for looking carefully at wet patches, and to prepare a sound programme for getting rid of them.

Filling in low ground   In small areas of low lying land which give rise to persistent problems, there is a temptation to dump in waste soil to raise the level of the land. Before this is done, it is important to examine the soil to see if any compact layers are present. These should be broken up before the in-fill is added; if left untreated the compact soil will persist and remain buried, now deeper below the new and higher surface. Moreover it may now be located below the reach of subsoilers and deep cultivators.

Iron ochre   Iron ochre is a rust coloured material formed when soluble forms of iron come into contact with air. In severe cases drains, whether plastic pipes or clay tiles, may be blocked within months of installation. This condition occurs in some peaty marsh and fen soils, though some acid sands also provide a source of soluble iron (ferrous ions). The iron is rendered soluble in the absence of air and when drains are introduced, air entry reverses the process. Complex chemical and microbial changes are involved to form a gelatinous or filamentous sludge in and around field drains; on drying this can become very hard.

The problem is intractable and there is no ready solution. Situations where it may occur can be forecast by soil examination. Typical examples are peaty clays in the Fens of East Anglia, and peaty or organic marshy soils alongside rivers. It is the combination of the presence of organic matter and prolonged periods of waterlogging which appears to be responsible for the formation of large amounts of iron in its soluble form. Field tests are available to detect ferrous ions.

If examination (and analysis) of the soil shows that a severe ochre problem is likely, the question must be asked whether field drainage would be worthwhile, since there is no guarantee that any techniques or treatment will be successful. If the decision is to go ahead, open ditching should be considered as an initial step, to provide drainage and allow air to enter and oxidize some of the iron without incurring blockage. If under-drainage is installed wide slot plastic pipes should be specified or, where clay tiles are used, the gap between them should be increased slightly. Once in place, the drains should be flushed by jetting immediately to deal with any initial ochre which forms. This should be repeated regularly, possibly at intervals of two months in the first winter. The need will be demonstrated by the quantity of ochre flushed out. Whenever ochre appears at the outfall, further flushing should be done.

It is particularly important to jet or rod thoroughly in spring before drains cease to run; if ochre is left to dry in the drains over the summer it will harden to a rigid deposit which may block slots and gaps and which may not be removable by later jetting.

Various chemical techniques have been proposed to control ochre problems but none so far appear to be adequately practical or successful. Iron ochre problems are found in many countries throughout the world and future research may yet find a solution.

Soil maps Since soil properties are one of the principal factors used in drainage design, soil maps have been used to derive drainage prediction maps. These show typical drainage solutions for each type of soil. The maps are not available for all areas; further details of the maps and the areas covered may be obtained from local Advisory Services and Soil Survey Offices.

Chapter 11   PROBLEMS RELATED TO CROP NUTRITION

To determine the nutrient status of a soil and the optimum quantity of fertilizer to apply is an important subject. There are many sources of sound advice, from State, independent and commercial organisations. A full discussion of all that is involved is beyond the scope of this book. Nevetheless, because nutrition is such a key part of good husbandry, several aspects are to be examined in this chapter, particularly where there are links to the physical state of the soil.

Leaching and other losses

In any climate where part of the rainfall each year leaches through the soil, anything soluble in water can be transferred to drains, streams or underground waters. Fortunately, there are processes whereby many plant nutrients are retained in the soil and not simply swept out in the water as it moves through. Nutrients which bear a positive charge (cations) such as calcium, potassium and magnesium, are held back to some degree by negative charges on clay and organic matter present in soils. Despite this mechanism, significant losses of these and smaller amounts of other soluble cations take place each year. Nutrients which are soluble and bear a negative charge are not restrained and move out readily in leaching water; these include nitrate, sulphate and chloride: generally very little phosphate is lost by leaching. There is nothing that can be done to prevent such losses. Leaching is an inexorable, natural process. Unless the losses are made good from the weathering and decomposition of rock fragments in the soil, or replaced by the application of lime, fertilizers or manures, then the land will gradually become impoverished and more acid.

Nutrients are also carried off the land in crops, livestock and in animal products such as milk and wool. Some nutrients, mainly nitrogen, are also lost in volatile forms from the soil and direct from plants though these are usually small amounts. The circumstances in which they may be significant are discussed below in the section on nitrogen. Burning straw or other crop residues can increase losses partly by converting some nutrients present in the crop to more soluble forms and partly by losses in smoke or as components made volatile by the heat.

Soil Acidity and Liming

In any climate where leaching occurs, all soils gradually become more acid unless lime is applied in appropriate amounts. An exception is where there are large reserves of carbonate in the soil as limestone or chalk, so that it may take many centuries to produce an acid soil on the surface. The practice of liming goes back to at least Roman times, long before the principles of crop nutrition were established or measurements made of soil acidity. Despite widespread knowledge of the need for lime, its ready availability and of the many organisations willing to test the soil, crop failure due to acid soil occurs regularly in all parts of the country. The reasons for these continuing crop failures are probably a combination of complacency, economics and inadequate testing of the most susceptible soils in a field.

Acidity is measured in soils by determining the pH value (the expression pH means literally 'the power of hydrogen'). Plants vary in their tolerance to pH. Of the commonly grown farm crops, the most intolerant of acid soils are lucerne, barley, sugar beet, beans, peas and red clover; those most tolerant to acid soils include rye, oats and potatoes. Crop tolerance also depends on other soil properties, particularly its organic matter content. On a highly organic or peaty soil, slightly lower pH values could be tolerated.

All soils can become acid, except those with reserves of carbonate present, mentioned earlier. However, sandy soils are more likely to develop patches of failed crop for several reasons. The proportion of water leaching through sandy soils is greater than through loamy or clayey soils, therefore a greater quantity of calcium and other nutrients can be lost. This is because sands retain less water compared to the other soils. Another reason is that sands have less ability to retain cations, including calcium and magnesium, by the mechanism discussed in the previous section. However, soils of all textures — sands, loams, clays and peats — may become so acid that crops fail.

The amount of lime required to increase the pH value of an acid soil to a desired level depends on how acid the soil is, the depth of soil that is acid, and on the type of soil. Less lime is required to increase the pH of a sandy soil, more to increase the pH of a clayey or peaty soil. The amount required can be determined by a laboratory test.

On soils known to become acid, the interval between applications of lime can vary between about four and ten years. One practical point of note is that it is better to anticipate when liming may be needed and to test the field and also the most susceptible areas separately, rather than to wait for acid patches to develop. Experience has shown that when soil, acid enough to cause crop failure, is limed, full recovery of crop performance may not take place in the year of application, due to the delay associated with incorporation and reaction between soil and lime. On the other hand, excessive applications are not recommended, as these may increase the soil pH to such a value that the availability of several nutrients is reduced, particularly manganese, thereby inducing deficiencies in the crop. The latter condition is also linked to the organic content of soils and is more severe on peaty and organic soils. Where patches of crop failure are thought to be associated with pH, it is essential to determine whether this is due to low or high values. Several cases are known where extra lime has been applied on patches where the failure was due to manganese deficiency, thereby making the condition worse.

There is little to choose between different sources of lime, which are sold on the basis of their TNV (Total Neutralising Value, a measure of chemical reactivity) and their fineness, an indication of how well they will mix into the soil and of their speed of reaction. One material, dolomitic or magnesian limestone, contains magnesium carbonate as well as calcium carbonate and is used where additional magnesium may be beneficial, principally on livestock farms.

Nitrogen

Nitrogen (N) is not only the nutrient which has most influence on crop growth, yield and quality, but it is also the most difficult for which to determine accurately the quantity required to produce the expected yield. The reason for this uncertainty is that a significant part of the crop's supply is provided from the decomposition of organic matter in the soil. Furthermore, once nitrogen has been converted to nitrate, it may be washed away by rain or converted to gaseous form in saturated soil and lost to the air. The search for a sound method of predicting the release of N from the soil has been arduous and long, but a system that is entirely satisfactory has so far eluded science. Predictions of the amount of N needed on a field-by-field basis are available from many sources — advisers, consultants, fertilizer suppliers and merchants. The recommended amounts are based on the results of many hundreds of experiments and can be used as a basic guide; search and research for greater accuracy continues. However, the hope that one setting of a fertilizer distributor can be made to apply N to one crop over the farm is unwise and unrealistic. Therefore, in this section, the technical background to some of the processes in the soil which are involved with gains and losses of N will be discussed.

Mineralisation

While plant roots are surrounded by large amounts of N in organic forms, up to 20 t/ha or more in some soils, this is virtually wholly unavailable to the plant until it is converted into mineral forms, ammonium and nitrate (mineralisation). This process occurs in two stages:

1. organic forms of N → ammonium

2. ammonium   → nitrate.

The first is mainly achieved by microbial action, though ammonium may also be formed without the intervention of microorganisms, notably when soils are heated, as for example under burning crop residues. The second is achieved by a two-stage microbial conversion.

From a practical viewpoint, the relative activity of microbial life governs how much N may be released. Under warm, moist, well aerated conditions, microbial activity may be intense and much N released into soluble forms; under cold, dry or water-logged conditions, very little. Significant amounts of N are not usually released until soil temperatures reach 7° C or more, so that any factors which influence temperature may affect the amount of N released e.g. air temperature, sunshine. Bare soil exposed to direct sun warms up more quickly than under a dense crop canopy, so the type of crop grown may also influence the production of mineral N from soils. A dark soil will warm up more quickly than a pale coloured soil when exposed to the sun. Cycles of wetting and drying increase the amounts of N mineralised to a greater extent than if the soil was either continually wet or continually dry. Other factors influencing the quantity of N mineralised are the amount and quality of soil organic matter present and the pH value of the soil. Highly organic and peaty soils tend to release large amounts of N, provided they are well aerated.

The amounts of N released in soils is variable but should be taken into account when assessing fertilizer need. Any crop residues or organic manures must also be broken down by the same mechanism, before the N they contain can be taken up by the crop. It is not yet possible to predict accurately the amount of N likely to be mineralised, but calculations involving the factors discussed earlier show much promise.

Range of typical amounts of N mineralised during the growing season:-

	kg/ha N
Mineral soils	20 − 80
Organic mineral soils	60 − 120
Lowland arable peat	100 − 300

The knowledge of local advisers, together with on-farm experience, should allow prediction of the expected values for a particular field by examining all of the factors involved:

- soil type − texture and depth
- organic content
- previous cropping and disposal of residues
- previous N applications in manures and fertilisers
- previous winter rainfall
- soil temperature.

**Nitrogen losses —
leaching and
denitrification**

Having made decisions on the quantity of supplementary N to apply at the beginning of the season, one must remain alert to the possibility of loss after application. The rate that a crop can take up N from the soil depends on the area of active leaf covering the surface of the land and on how fast the crop is growing. About 2 kg/ha per day would be enough to satisfy the needs of most crops growing normally in early summer. If a large amount of N was present in the soil, up to 6 kg/ha per day may be taken up, but the crop may gain little or no benefit from the extra supply. If the crop has just emerged, uptake of N will be proportionately much less, and the uptake will also be smaller in cold weather when growth is slow.

Without discussing the complexities of the relationships between N application and growth at different stages of crop development, applications of N which are much greater than current crop need are at risk from loss. The major losses may be due to heavy rainfall or to waterlogging of the soil. Heavy rain may wash out some of the N applied, putting it beyond the reach of crop roots. Such displacement is usually significant only on sandy soils. If the land becomes saturated on the surface and air is excluded, nitrate can decompose to gaseous forms (denitrification) if the saturation of the soil continues for more than a few hours. The effects of lack of aeration on N supply can often be seen in wet hollows where a pale, stunted, N deficient crop is the result. This effect is also commonly seen in badly poached pastures, which often show pale growth. The death of roots may also be partly responsible in these two examples, for poor growth. The severity of loss by denitrification in saturated soil is enhanced in warm weather because of the greater activity of soil microorganisms. It is also more severe when oxygen entry is restricted by soil compaction. Yellow N deficient crop growth is frequently seen in a regular pattern across fields in late spring, associated with compaction under wheeltracks. It must also be stressed that all nitrate in the soil is prone to loss by leaching or decomposition by denitrification, whether it comes from fertilizer or was derived from plant residues, native soil organic matter or organic manures.

Whenever land has lain wet and sodden for a few days in late spring or summer, the possibility of substantial loss of nitrate by denitrification must be considered. Practical experience suggests that losses of up to 5 kg/ha per day or even more are possible. Subsequent observations on the growth and colour of the crop may indicate a shortage of N, and be confirmed by tests of crop or soil. It must be a matter of local judgement whether to apply more N, depending on the area involved, access, the stage of crop development, and the value of the crop. If the area is small, replacement N can be spread by hand, action which has given effective results in several cases examined by the author.

Nitrogen losses — volatilisation

In hot dry weather nitrogen can be lost from the surface of the land as gaseous ammonia, following recent applications of fertilizers containing urea or ammonium forms of nitrogen, to limestone, chalk or other calcareous soils, or to land recently limed. The loss can be as high as 20% or more of the N applied. However, if the N applied is either injected into the soil, or is incorporated quickly, losses would be negligible. Substantial losses of ammonia can also follow heavy application of organic manures and slurries which are spread in dry hot weather. This is considered to be one of the largest losses of N in U K agriculture. Some of the N in urine voided by grazing animals is lost in this way.

Pollution of soil and water

It is the responsibility of every farmer to ensure that no action, inadvertant or otherwise, leads to pollution of the soil or to water draining from the land, whether in drains, streams or in underground water bearing rocks. In relation to good soil husbandry, the correct use of nitrogen fertilizer includes its use in such a way that nitrate losses are minimal. It is not only wasteful to let nitrate 'go down the drain' but damaging to the quality of potable water supplies in both the short term and long term. Similarly, the disposal of slurry and manures must also be done using quantities and under conditions which allow the soil to absorb the application without direct pollution to taint waters leaving the land. In addition, the subsequent production of nitrate from the manure must not be excessive so that contamination of water supplies results.

Another group of chemicals which may pollute the soil are known as 'heavy metals'; these include lead, mercury, zinc, copper, cadmium and chromium. Their direct use in agriculture is now almost non-existent but they are present in some sewage products and other wastes which are spread on the land for disposal. The quantity that may be applied to the land is the subject of regulations by the EEC and the supplier is required to provide information on any pollutants present.

Chapter 12

LAND QUALITY AND LAND USE

The way land is used is partly due to what it is capable of growing, and partly due to the individual choice of the farmer. To this must be added the constraints imposed by planning regulations and those of plant health. In some areas there may be specific limitations such as in National Parks, in areas used for water gathering, sites of Special Scientific Interest and Environmentally Sensitive Areas.

The biological restraints to the choice of crops

Climate is a primary limitation. No bananas are grown on the slopes of Snowdonia where the rainfall may be adequate but the temperature is much too low. The plants available for commercial exploitation outdoors have been selected from native and imported species for their suitability in a particular climate, and their performance and characteristics have been refined by plant breeders. The principal species selected for cropping in Britain are grasses, clovers, cereals, peas, beans, potatoes, sugar beet and members of the brassica family, turnips, swedes, rape and kale. Whatever new crops are introduced, they are still subject to the restraints of mean and maximum temperature, rainfall, frost and the length of the growing season.

If left to Nature, most land in the U K would revert to forest and scrub, though at present, trees occupy about 9% of the country. Large areas are covered with rough grazing, the official designation for open moorland and unimproved grassland used mainly for sheep grazing. These are where natural restraints are severe and largely preclude other forms of agricultural land use.

Temperature and rainfall (and to a lesser extent exposure) are largely responsible for the pattern of land use in the U K. Crops which require a higher temperature or longer season for

Table 12.1 Land use in the U.K in 1972 and 1986
(Area, Million Hectares)

	1972	1986
Wheat	1.13	2.00
Barley	2.29	1.92
Oats	0.31	0.09
Total Cereals	3.80	4.03
Potatoes	0.22	0.18
Sugar Beet	0.19	0.20
Oilseed Rape	0.007	0.30
Vegetables (outdoor)	0.18	0.14
Total Tillage	4.86	5.29
Grass, short term, less than 5 years	2.36	1.72
Grass, long term, 5 years old & over	4.91	5.08
Rough Grazings	6.61	6.05
Forests	1.97	2.27

The total area of the U.K is approximately 24.5 Mha and of this about 18.4 Mha (75%), is used for agriculture.

(Figures based on MAFF and Forestry Commission statistics)

growth are confined to the south, for example, maize, vines, cherries. All crops require water in amounts adequate to meet peak demands in summer and those grown on sandy or shallow soils in areas of low rainfall are at risk and crop yields are erratic unless irrigated. For example, the sandy heaths of the Suffolk Coast is one such area, much of which is not in agricultural use, and supports natural or semi-natural vegetation as an attractive amenity.

Where rainfall is greater, a wider range of soils may be used for arable cropping, up to a maximum of about 1000 mm annually. Rainfall higher than this is associated with later harvests and wetter soils so that arable crops are largely restricted to those grown for forage.

Good soil husbandry begins with choosing crops which are suited to the climate, and which will perform well and consistently in all but the most extreme of seasons.

Physical restraints to the choice of crop Two physical factors, slope and soil, present restraints to land use not because crops are biologically incapable of being grown, but because of the techniques of present-day agriculture. Arable machinery is rarely used on slopes steeper than 1 in 9 but in other areas of the world, crops may be grown on slopes much steeper by tilling with animals or by using manual labour, particularly for terracing. Clay soils present a restraint to root crops and potatoes not because of low yields but because separation of soil and crop is difficult with conventional mechanical methods of harvest, particularly in wet weather.

Wet soils, whatever their origin, affect both crop growth and soil management; they may be too soft for machinery to travel over without damaging the soil, and crops may not grow well because of poor root development in saturated conditions. Field drainage is therefore a key factor in land use.

Current land use Table 12.1 shows the use of land in Britain in 1986 compared with 1972, the year before the U K joined the European Community. The political influence is shown by the large increase in the area of oilseed rape.

Land quality The concept that land has a capability for cropping, for pasture or forestry which, if exceeded, presents considerable risks was one of the products of research following the dustbowl disasters of N America in the 1920s and 1930s. The severity of restraints due to climate, soil and slope provides a basis for the assessment of land quality. Good soil husbandry must take into account the suitability of land for the crop chosen, coupled with knowledge of the technology available for its management.

The natural variability of soils often means that land of dissimilar properties and quality occurs in the same field. This makes more difficult the choice of crop and its cultivation. Some variation may be reduced by, for example, drainage of a low wet area, but little can be done when soils of contrasting texture occur within the same field, for example a sandy loam and a clay. The trend towards greater field size may make problems related to soil variability worse, since field boundaries have often been located by our forebears to coincide with boundaries between two different types of soil. The author has examined several cases where poor crop growth occurred in a distinct area which had formerly been a separate field; cultivations suited to one part were ill-suited to the other, and damaging soil compaction resulted. Thus the benefits of a greater work-rate on a larger field may be negated if crop loss occurs or separate management is required on part of the land.

There is no doubt that small areas of land that are different, within an otherwise uniform field, are a nuisance. Such awkward spots are sometimes given obsessive and uneconomic attention in an attempt to superimpose uniformity of use on a naturally variable landscape. Unless maintained, reversion may occur and the idea of letting nature take over to create a variety of habitats can provide a visually attractive alternative.

The sections which follow draw attention to the key role of soil husbandry in using land efficiently and summarize some of the critical points of each major system of land use.

Upland grazings   Few options are available in wet cold climates with a short summer and a long winter. Both plants and animals are adapted to survive and land use is dominated by sheep farming, with some cattle. In some areas there is also a significant contribution to the economy from grouse and deer. Forestry is an alternative except on higher and exposed land unsuited to trees.

Apart from the direct effects of severe weather there are two periods of the year when sheep respond to improved nutrition. One is at mating in autumn, for without conception there can be no progeny; the other is a period before and after lambing. Better quality in-bye pastures are reserved for these periods, supplemented by forage roots or bought-in feed. In terms of soil husbandry, the more productive intensively used in-bye land should be capable of being grazed when the stock need the extra nutrition. This may require drainage to provide a firm surface and to reduce poaching risks so that heavy rain will not prevent access. Shelter and aspect also influence the value of in-bye land. Where reclamation of hill land to better pasture is contemplated, areas with fewer restrictions should be considered first as the costs of improvement could be less, for example by choosing better drained land, south facing and gentle slopes. It is not always necessary to improve all the land uniformly within an enclosure to bring about a worthwhile increase in production. In wet regions, losses of lime from reclaimed land can be high and little-and-often can give good results at an economic cost. Reclamation is not a once and for all treatment in hill areas and unless plant nutrition is maintained, pastures can revert.

There are several situations where soil examination can identify limits to production in upland soils. For example, good results have been obtained in the Southwest of England following the breaking of a thin layer of iron cemented soil which was found to be limiting root growth.

Grassland   Grass can grow from sea level to over 600 m in Britain, and within an annual rainfall from 600 mm to over 1500 mm. In the drier lowlands grass is confined mainly to land physically incapable of tillage because it is too rough, too steep or too stoney and to river banks and land prone to flooding. There are also significant areas of grass as Parks, Parklands around stately homes, racing and riding establishments, sportsfields, golf courses and road verges.

Most grass used for agriculture is consumed where it grows by grazing livestock. Production centres on the supply of N and water, derived from soil reserves plus the input from rain, irrigation, fertilizers and manures. Utilisation centres on controlled grazing and the avoidance of poaching to compact the soil and damage the sward.

Grass has a well established and well deserved reputation for protecting the surface of the land and improving soil structure. However, in its establishment, grass is as sensitive to poor structure as any other small-seeded crop. An example of the adverse effects of compact soil close to the surface on grass establishment is given in Figure 8.3.

The other main aspect of grass production in relation to soil husbandry is poaching — damage to the sward and soil from hoof pressure applied when the ground is soft — which was discussed in Chapter 8. In relation to land capability, drainage is a key factor in grass utilisation, particularly if intensively grazed. For consistent high production, naturally well drained soils are preferred. Where drainage is needed, special attention should be paid to gateways, access tracks and water troughs. When very wet weather occurs in summer, the driest land should be used. Alternatively, stock may be housed temporarily. However, it should be recognised that some soils which are slow draining and difficult to drain effectively may not be suited to intensive grazing in high rainfall areas.

Arable cropping Whilst not native to Britain, but originally from drier and warmer climates of the Middle East, cereals have adapted well to temperate conditions. They are the most deep-rooted of our annual crops, and in suitable soils roots can reach a depth of 2 m; this characteristic is undoubtedly inherited from the development of the species in a climate where little rain may fall between sowing and harvest. During the summer grain-filling phase, yield is influenced by the amount of sunshine, and in a dull year yields will be below average, irrespective of all other factors. The upper limit of annual rainfall for successful cereal cropping is about 1000 mm.

There are few restrictions for cereal growing due to soil properties. Cereals can be grown in soils of all textures, from sands to clays. However, yields may be restricted in sands, sometimes severely, in areas of large soil moisture deficit, for example the sands of Norfolk, Suffolk and Surrey. Clays in drier areas have proved well suited to autumn sown cereals and consistent yields have been obtained.

Autumn sowing differs from spring sowing in a number of ways. In autumn, soils are warmer and drier below the surface, providing good conditions for root growth. In clays the summer cracks will not yet have closed up, so roots can readily locate pathways for downward penetration. In spring, soils are colder and wetter below the surface and conditions are less favourable for root growth. In clays, all cracks in the subsoil will have closed up and will remain so until crops extract water to initiate shrinkage. There is also a greater risk of soil damage in spring during cultivation or sowing, because of the wetter subsurface conditions compared to the drier state of land in early autumn. This difference in the state of the soil in autumn and spring may be one reason why problems related to soil compaction appear to be less evident where there is a preponderance of autumn sown crops.

The most extensively grown of the other arable crops are oil seed rape, potatoes, sugar beet, peas and beans. These, and the many alternatives now grown, will be grouped into two as far as land use and soil husbandry is concerned; those harvested above ground, mainly by combine, and those extracted from the ground.

Apart from harvest method, there is one other important difference; root crops have a high content of water and the mass to be taken off the land is three to five times (or more) greater than for grain or seed crops. More loaded trailers have to cross the land with consequent compaction under their tracks. Cereals should present few hazards to the soil, provided that care is taken over a number of basic points:

● Acidity − test soils regularly and correct as necessary, particularly for barley

● Drainage − install and maintain to avoid wet patches

● Timing of land work − try to avoid working the land when it is wet and soft, unless it is unavoidable

● Soil examination − undertake regular checks and plan remedial cultivation as and when needed

● Tramlines and harvest tracks − break up compaction to reduce erosion on slopes and ponding in hollows.

Obviously, other factors may be important in specific fields, such as disease, pests, weeds and trace element deficiencies.

Root crops and potatoes, however, need more care. Seedbeds require intensive preparation to meet the conditions needed for sowing small seeded crops such as sugar beet. Potatoes are pre ferably grown in a stone-free and clod-free ridge to reduce damage at harvest and to avoid contamination of the produce. The risks to soils are not so much at planting but at lifting. To reduce the risks, root crops and potatoes should be grown on land that drains well, and of no more than moderate clay content. If the clay content is high, stickiness in wet conditions leads to traction difficulties and adhesion of soil to the crop. On such soils, the risks of damage may be reduced by lifting the crop early when the soil is drier. For potatoes, there is a further hazard; burning off the tops a few weeks before lifting means that soils gradually become wetter because there is no longer foliage to extract water from the soil.

The key points for root crops, potatoes and late season vegetable crops are:

● Selection of land suitable − avoid slow-draining soils and those of high clay content;

● Soil examination − check prior to cropping and deal with any compact layers that may hold up water;

● Cultivation − plan well ahead in the previous autumn, avoid compaction or smearing at planting;

● Planter or spray wheelings − if water tends to run into hollows, break up wheel compaction in the furrow with a narrow tine ;

● Harvest − plan same-day tillage after lifting to break up compaction below tracks.

Organic farming   Land given over to production based on the principles of organic farming relies heavily on organic materials as sources of nutrients for crops and grass. These include manures, slurries, composts and organic fertilizers as well as soil organic matter and residues from previous crops. Only a small proportion of the nutrients which these sources contain is immediately available to the plant. The remainder requires the process of mineralization to break down the organic matter and convert the nutrients into soluble forms that can be taken up by crop plants. This process is microbial and therefore the rate is governed by the factors affecting microbial growth. The two most important are temperature and aeration. Below a temperature of about 7^0 C in the soil, mineralisation is insignificant. Therefore in the northern parts of Britain and in the cooler uplands, it may be unwise to rely solely on organic sources for plant nutrition. Soil aeration is a vital necessity where mineralisation is the major process controlling crop nutrition. In the absence of oxygen, mineralisation will be insignificant. Any action on the farm which creates an oxygen deficit in the soil will be likely to have severe effects in organic farming — more so than with conventional methods.

The sensitivity of organically farmed soils to aeration means that the principles of soil husbandry and soil examination are even more relevant than under conventional farming where any shortage of N may be replaced with readily soluble sources in the form of fertilizers.

Soil over-compaction, whether due to machinery pressure on soft soils, or to the poaching of livestock and ineffective drainage, could have marked effects. It is also important to note that the oxygen demand is enhanced within soils of higher organic matter content, and particularly in those to which organic manures have been applied, so that the effects of a restriction of oxygen supply would be consequently even greater.

However, some forms of organic farming permit N fertilisers of certain types to be used, for example calcium ammonium nitrate, and sodium nitrate. The current regulations for specific types of organic farming would provide details of rates and formulation of permitted materials.

Trees   A tree requires water and nutrients just as any other plant, but differs from annual crops or grass in several important ways. The density of plants per unit area required for woodland or orchard is much less. In the early years tree seedlings may be subject to competition from other plants of greater height, for light, or water and nutrients from the soil. For a tree, the period from planting to maturity may be 40, 60 or even over 100 years. Because of this long period, it is imperative that the species chosen is suited to the quality of the land, particularly the soil properties. Any limitations in the physical condition of the soil must be dealt with prior to planting because there is no possibility of remedial cultivation during the life of the crop. Root anchorage against wind is a key consideration, and where dense layers in the subsoil restrict soil-root volume, deep cultivation is needed to break up the compact soil.

Where a mixture of trees and other crops or grass is grown, the partition of sunshine between the two would be proportional to the area of each canopy intercepting the light. More trees − less grass. The author recalls investigating the low production of grass from a delightful area of mature traditional parkland; a simple calculation showed that the land directly shaded by the tree canopies was about 14% of the field area. Competition for water could also have reduced grass yields, as the roots of mature trees extend for considerable distances from the bole, at least as far as the canopy. Under large individual trees, or under a dense forest canopy, the soil may be devoid of vegetation at ground level.

Trees have many functions, as well as the production of timber − visual amenity, shelter, windbreak, erosion control, wildlife habitats and livestock containment. A wide range of species, both native and exotic, are available and suited to virtually every environment except those most exposed to severe winds. If left to nature, almost the whole of our lowland landscape would revert to trees.

Chapter 13 — LAND RESTORATION AND RECLAMATION

This chapter concentrates on the principles of land restoration and highlights a number of difficulties encountered in particular situations. The period that the land is out of use from agriculture can vary from a few weeks in the case of a small diameter pipeline, to several years for mineral extraction, such as sand, gravel or opencast coal and to a century or more for some industrial sites. Where disturbance of the land has yet to begin, it is possible to obtain detailed information on soil properties and land quality on which to base a working plan and also to enable a comparison to be made of the site condition before working and after restoration. If no prior survey is done comparisons of restored land can sometimes be made against similar land adjacent to the site.

When the period of alternative use is lengthy, none of the original soil may be left for restoration, as in the case of residual dereliction of Victorian industries. In these cases, it may be a question of trying to create a new soil which is capable of supporting plant life, from whatever is available locally. Topsoil from other land may be brought in but it is rarely available in sufficient quantities or at an economic cost. Subsoil or even overburden can be used as a surface covering which, with skill, care and considerable time, may eventually weather into soil of adequate quality, as discussed later in this chapter.

In almost all current restoration, local planning authorities are involved. They may initiate the restoration of derelict, despoiled or unwanted industrial sites and for proposed mineral extraction, planning consent would include a requirement to restore to a specific after-use, not necessarily the original use of the land. Conditions of working, control of the local environment, and evaluation and approval of the completed restoration are usually also the responsibility of the planning department, who can call on other local authority or Government Departments for appropriate technical help.

Prior examination of site

Wherever possible, it is desirable to obtain a detailed and accurate survey of the soils and landscape. This survey should pay particular attention to the following:

● topsoil quality and quantity − its depth and a full description of its physical properties;

● subsoil − its depth and full description of physical properties to at least 1.7 m below the surface, unless a barrier such as rock is encountered;

● soil distribution − where more than one type of soil is found over the site, the distribution of each must be presented on a map;

● land drainage − details of all field drains and ditches;

● terrain characteristics − detailed plan showing contours at 1 m intervals.

The information obtained will enable land quality to be assessed as a base-line against which to compare any subsequent restoration. It can indicate also the quantities of soil on-site, so that a sound working plan can be prepared.

Site working

The area, shape, depth, drainage and whether materials are to be extracted or deposited, will largely dictate the engineering requirements of each site. Soils are usually regarded as superficial layers, but their attributes should not be disregarded, nor should they be treated as inert rock-like fragments. If sequential working and simultaneous replacement of soils is not possible, all materials to be stored should be handled with care; soils are porous and fragile, and should not be severely compressed at any stage. In addition, they should be handled, i.e. lifted, transported and heaped, when in a dry condition; if handled wet, severe and irreversible changes may result. Topsoil should remain porous when stored so that aeration can continue, heaps should be

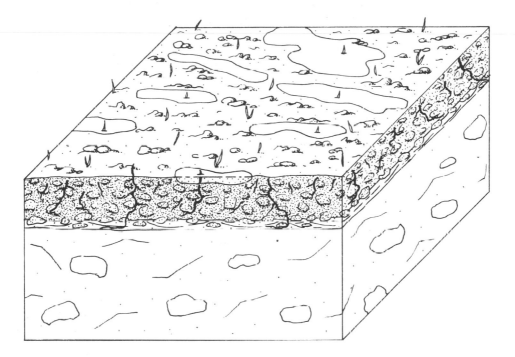

FIGURE 13.1 *Effect of Unbroken Over-compact Soil on Land Recently Restored from Gravel Workings*

The topsoil had been carefully replaced, prepared as a seedbed and grass sown. The first rain could not drain through, water ponded on the surface to produce a soft slurried condition. The subsoil was extremely dense, hard and impervious, but when subsequently broken by deep cultivation, drainage improved and the grass grew normally.

restricted in height to 1.5 m if possible, a rough and ridged heap would be preferable to one smooth topped, soil is better dumped loosely and left; any heap should not be run over with dumpers or bulldozers.

Restoration

Once extraction or filling is complete and the final landscape prepared, the initial need is to plan drainage. If the restored overburden (i.e. the material originally below the subsoil) is likely to be porous, any compaction of its surface should be fractured before the subsoil is replaced. If not done at this stage, the compact surface may be eventually beyond the depth of tilling equipment once the subsoil has been placed on top. Replacement of the subsoil should be done in dry conditions, preferably by dumping loosely with minimum handling and surface compaction from tracked or wheeled vehicles. Any unavoidable compaction should be broken up before the topsoil is replaced. When compact soil which contains many stones is to be loosened, the angle of the tine used to break up the dense layer should be backward raking; if forward-raking, many stones may be lifted upwards to obtrude on to the surface.

Assessment of restoration quality

In the past, the quality of restoration was frequently poor, when compared with the original or adjacent land. The quantity of soil retained for replacement was sometimes less than that originally present, and the quality may have been reduced by loss or by dilution with stones or overburden. Compaction was a frequent cause of poor drainage and indifferent crop growth.

In order to assess the quality of land restoration, a number of trenches should be dug with a mechanical digger to a depth appropriate to the site in question, perhaps 1 − 1.2 m. Because of the frequency of hard layers encountered, hand digging is both difficult and time consuming. This examination should be done before the first crop is established, often grass, so that any residual compaction can be attended to prior to sowing. A further check can be made in a similar way after a year or more, when the roots of the crop can be used to indicate any residual compaction, and also the presence of any surface or subsurface water visible after rain.

Special situations: To some extent each site has its own problems but there are a number of points, some general, some specific, that can be made in relation to land restoration.

1. Plant nutrition. Because the normal organic cycle is interrupted when soils are moved, stored, compacted and replaced, additional nitrogen is almost always needed in the first few years after restoration whether the land is used for grass, arable or amenity crops. This can be most conveniently given as nitrogen fertilizer, in frequent doses as required to maintain plant growth and vigour. Yellow stunted growth is commonly a sign of N deficiency, though if seen in patches the soil should also be examined physically to see if residual compaction is present, and also analysed chemically to see if other nutrients or lime are deficient. Farmyard manure or sewage sludge may also be used, particularly at sites where little topsoil was available.

2. Toxic sites. On some sites reclaimed from land used for mining, smelting, processing, or storing metals or chemicals, specific toxic residues may remain in sufficient quantities to affect plant growth. Expert sampling, analyses and interpretation may be needed. Much can be done to reduce the availability of some metals, e.g. copper and zinc, by adjusting the pH value.

3. Pyrites. Spoil from deep mined coal and from organic shales may contain pyrites (iron sulphide), which can oxidize to produce sulphuric acid. Some reclaimed spoil heaps have been affected by this problem, with severe acidity killing grass or trees in patches a few years after re-instatement. The acid may also leach downwards and come to the surface on the side or edge of a heap, and adversely affect the vegetation or water quality in ditches leading from the site.

4. Power station fly ash. The fine particles of ash left after pulverised coal is burnt have several industrial uses, but most is put into lagoons or heaps. The final surface is usually planted with grass or trees, often with little topsoil. Much success has been achieved, provided compaction, drainage and nutrition are attended to. Some coals produce an ash containing high levels of soluble boron. These may remain high enough during the first few years after restoration to affect some plant species adversely.

5. No-soil sites. On sites where no topsoil has been left for replacement, the cost of buying from elsewhere and transporting it may be prohibitive, assuming supplies can be obtained. The alternative is to attempt to produce soil by natural soil forming processes, working with whatever is available on the site. This requires the skill of the soil scientist to select the most weatherable materials, and to prepare them physically and chemically for the introduction of suitable plant species. Trees are often more adaptable to such situations, but grasses can also establish. Regular nutrition, particuarly of N, may be needed; drought may be a problem if the subsurface is impervious. The addition of bulky organic matter such as farmyard manure, slurry or good quality sewage products may do much to encourage soil development. Where the site to be reclaimed is very rocky with a low rate of weathering, trees may be able to obtain an adequate foothold, if a little soil is provided in the planting hole. In many no-soil or low-soil sites, trees may be much more tolerant than grass, though on-site evaluation is recommended to determine which species grows best.

Chapter 14   PHYSICAL EXAMINATION OF SOILS IN THE FIELD

One of the principal objectives of SOIL HUSBANDRY is to demonstrate that examination of the physical state of a soil should be a regular and normal part of farm management. Soil analysis is well established as a guide to liming and fertilizer practice and soil examination should have at least an equal role. The correct and complete functioning of the whole depth of soil below a crop should be one of the primary tenets of good husbandry. The ploughman's foot no longer treads the furrow. The tractor driver now sits detached some distance above the soil and must be encouraged to climb down to examine the need for, and the effects of, the work being done. To make best use of soil resources, it is also worthwhile for all levels of management to be involved in their husbandry, from owner to tractor driver, and for all to share in both the collection of information and in its evaluation and use.

Many photographs and sketches have been used throughout the book to illustrate a variety of soil conditions. In this key Chapter dealing with the techniques of soil examination in the field, frequent reference is made to those used earlier, where appropriate.

When to look?   The cultivation season begins immediately after harvest when decisions must be made on getting the land ready for the next crop. Another time of peak interest is in spring, when seedbeds for spring sowing or planting must be prepared. These are often busy times and for many purposes there is no reason why examination should not be made at other times of the year, indeed there may be advantages in doing so. For some purposes, specific times should be selected: for drainage assessments, autumn or winter; to look for soil pans and to assess their effects, spring or early summer would be preferred, when roots of crops are approaching their maximum extension. However, at any time of the year information of significance may be obtained.

An important method of assessing the overall state of the soil is to look at the land when the soil is under stress, so that its reaction to extreme conditions may be observed and recorded. Two circumstances are particularly useful: when the weather has been very wet, and the reverse, during a drought. The reaction of soil to heavy rain can provide information on the stability of soil structure, on drainability and porosity of the soil and on its erodibility. Thus information can be obtained directly on soil conditions which cannot readily be obtained by other methods. For future use, it is well worth recording both the severity of a rainstorm and how the soil has been affected. If the surface of the land is bare, the degree of breakdown of structure and the degree of slumping can be determined, noted and photographed. The porosity of the soil and the significance of any compact layers may be assessed by systematically walking the land after heavy rain and testing the softness of the surface. A scale for the relative softness of the surface is given later in this chapter. The location of land lying wet, or with pools on the surface can be noted and the soil examined in these areas in greater detail when dry conditions return.

At times of drought, the 'hot spots' of shallow, rocky or gravelly land show up regularly, as pale, stunted crops. However, similar crop stress due to lack of water can also occur as a result of restrictions in root depth caused by soil compaction. If rain comes soon enough, some recovery in crop growth may occur, and it is worth noting whether the final yield is reduced. Photographs can be an excellent means of recording permanently the distribution of areas affected by drought, waterlogging or other problem which can be seen on the surface of the soil or in the appearance of the crop. Photographs can be taken at field level, from high ground or buildings, or from the air and can be used subsequently to locate areas for detailed soil examination.

Where to look?   To a large extent the location depends on the reason for the examination. Unless the diagnosis of a specific problem is the objective, then care should be taken to avoid gateways, tracks, headlands, wheelings and other disturbed ground. A typical

−1m

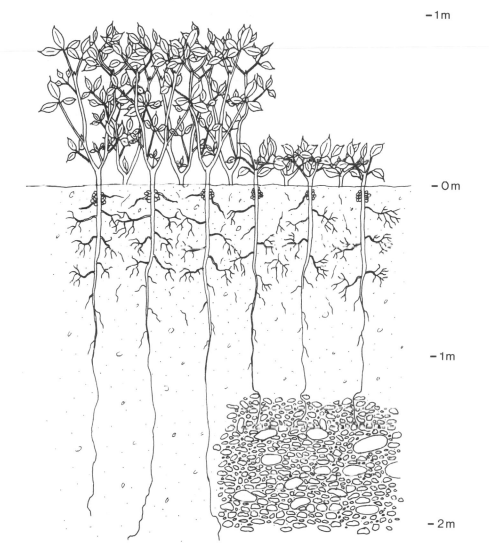

−0m

−1m

−2m

FIGURE 14.1 Growth of Lucerne Related to Natural Soil Variation.

After a dry summer and after three cuts of lucerne had been taken, the re-growth showed a sharp difference in height across the field; the soil was fine sandy loam and of normal structure to a depth of 1.0 m under both good and poor growth. A difference in soil properties was not revealed until a depth of 1.2 m, when the roots of the poor crop reached gravel, showing that the re-growth was related to reserves of water accessible to each crop.

piece of land should be selected, uniform in appearance and one or more holes dug.

How to look?

To the uninitiated, there is often reluctance to begin and a degree of hesitation and uncertainty that only experience will remove. Every soil can tell a story of its past and present; there is no mystique and with patient observation a great deal can be learnt.

If many areas are to be examined, consideration should be given to the use of a mechanical digger. These readily-hired machines are particularly useful if soils are dry or if much deep examination is required. For example in drainage investigations or if the effects of, or need for, deep cultivation are to be assessed. Otherwise a clean sharp spade is the tool to use, occasionally a pick or crowbar may also be needed. A soil auger may be used to extract soil from depth.

The dimensions of a hole depend on the question being asked and on how far the deepest zone of interest lies below the surface. Rarely would the depth be less than 50 cm and it could be up to 1 metre or more (Figure 14.1). It is usually better to make it deep rather than shallow, so that there is enough space at the bottom of the hole to accept waste soil taken off the face during examination. While digging, keep at least two edges of the hole untrampled; pile up soil dug out well away on the other sides. The next step is to prepare a vertical face so that the physical characteristics of the soil can be highlighted. Careful work must be done to show up many of the finer details some of which may have been obscured by smearing during excavation. Begin at the surface, probe and flick with a penknife or trowel and work down the face to restore natural features and to search for any man-induced changes. Where coarse blocky structure is found, an alternative method is to lever out spadesful of earth from the sides of the pit beginning near the base.

Where a mechanical digger is used, a trench can be dug readily to a depth of 1.5 m or more, to provide a hole deep enough and wide enough to walk along and to have topsoil almost at eye level. It can be very informative to cut such a trench across the normal direction of cultivation so that any compaction related to wheel track patterns can be more readily identified.

If compaction of the soil just below plough or cultivation depth is suspected, most of the loose soil above can be carefully removed by spade, or trowel and the last remnants lying on the upper surface of the suspect compact layer brushed or flicked off into the hole.

On completion of the examination, the soil must be replaced and the land surface left level, neither dished nor proud. Any large stones dug out should be put into the bottom of the pit. On grassland, the subsoil should be compressed by treading so that when turves are replaced they do not stick above the surface. Any surface compaction in the vicinity of the hole due to treading should be loosened.

What to look for – examination and interpretation

To assess soil properties, it is convenient to divide the soil into a number of layers: the soil surface, the layer disturbed by normal cultivations, the soil just below the cultivated soil and subsoil which is undisturbed by normal cultivations. Several different layers may be found in the subsoil.

One test applicable to each layer is that of soil texture which is one of the most useful tests to be done in the field. The technique of determining soil texture by hand assessment is described in Chapter 3. It gives a guide to many properties, e.g. water relationships, workability, structure type and stability. Marked changes in texture occurring within a profile should be noted as they can have a considerable influence on water movement and root growth.

The soil surface

Even before the hole is dug, the surface of soil can be examined. Does it appear to be porous or can signs of a disintegrated or compact structure be detected as a partially smooth or entirely smooth surface? Such a condition is more commonly found when a soil is bare and has been exposed to heavy rain (Figure 9.1). The presence of such a layer on the surface may be confirmed by probing and levering up the surface with a pointed blade (Figure 4.7). When wet a cap may seal the surface, and as it dries may become hard, often seen as a pale coloured crust. More stable aggregates and large mineral particles such as coarse sand or small stones can sometimes be seen firmly bound into the crust and projecting above the otherwise smooth surface

(Figure 5.1). Below a cap, aggregates can be seen firmly attached to the underside of the crusted portion. Soils with a high content of fine or very fine sand and silt, particularly where the organic matter content is low, are prone to show this feature, seen as a layer a few mm thick. If rain is heavy and prolonged or the land is flooded for a while, a cap may develop into a layer 3 − 5 cm thick (Figure 9.2).

Within the cultivated layer

This refers to the layer disturbed by cultivation, usually to a depth of 20 − 25 cm from the surface. The term 'cultivation' here includes all operations whether done by ploughs, disc or tine harrows, rotary or tine cultivators.

Soil pans

Almost any 'cultivation' can create a thin zone of compressed soil just below its operating depth and can also separate the original soil into a loosened state with firmer undisturbed soil below. The signs and effects of panning depend on the severity of the conditions and on the season. In wet weather at any time of the year, a smeared layer may hold up water and above it may be found wetter or waterlogged soil. Sometimes this effect can be identified by water seeping out of the soil above and running down the wall of the hole. A smeared layer can often be seen from above as a smooth, slightly shiny surface which may be continuous or discontinuous, and it may show an imprint of the blade or pressure face responsible for its formation. A thicker panned layer may be identified as a zone 1 − 2 cm thick where the original soil aggregates have been tightly packed together into a slab of obviously dense soil. Other changes may also accompany soil compaction; for example, dark grey anaerobic pockets with a distinct smell may be seen where recent crop residues have been incorporated into the compact soil. During summer and in dry weather a soil pan may be detected as a dry hard layer (Figure 8.3). The soil may be relatively moist below it and very dry in and above it, due to the inability of crop roots to penetrate and extract the moisture below (Figure 2.2). This 'moisture profile' is a useful test to supplement observations on soil density and root distribution and to confirm or refute the effects that a pan is having on the crop. In dry weather, the shrinkage which takes place in clay soils may fracture a pan, enabling roots to gain entry to the soil below. In sandy soils with no shrinkage, even relatively thin pans may persist throughout the season and

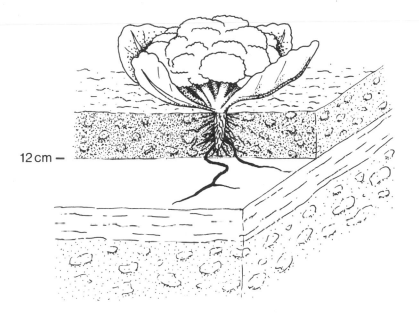

12 cm —

FIGURE 14.2 The Effect of a Classical Soil Pan on the Growth of Cauliflowers.

Examination of the soil under an area of poor crop, found a fine, porous and well aggregated structure to a depth of 12 cm, with many roots present; below that was a hard dense layer 4 cm thick with a smooth upper surface, roots ran across it but did not grow into it or through it into the loose unconsolidated soil below. The dense panned layer had been formed by tillage done under wet soil conditions.

have marked effects on crop growth. Thick pans usually have a greater adverse effect than thin but the depth at which they occur is important, with shallow pans having more severe effects. On very sandy soils an unusual method to detect thin compact layers is to remove carefully an entire spadeful when dry and lay it on its side; then give the edge several good 'puffs' of breath to remove loose sand. If compact layers are present they will then show up clearly as thin or thick ribs lying parallel to the surface.

Wet zones   Where drainage is restricted by a compact or smeared layer there is the increased risk of further compaction being caused by later cultivations. It is therefore important to realize the significance of relatively thin pans and to carefully identify them to determine their origin. Soils of all types may exhibit smeared layers, even sands and peats. On sloping land, if water cannot drain through a pan, the risk of erosion is considerably enhanced.

The separation of fine sand grains from aggregates can be used as a measure of structure instability in some soils. The detached particles may be seen as white, pale grey or pale yellowish-brown grains, collected in thin layers or pockets within the tilled layer and often found at the base of the cultivation depth.

Anaerobic conditions in the soil may be identified visually as blue-grey pockets or layers and when broken apart a characteristic sewage-like smell can be detected. Such conditions are usually more severe where straw, turf, sugar beet tops or other organic material is incorporated into the soil to provide a ready source of food for microbial life in the soil.

The presence of stones and clods may be of importance when assessing cultivation needs or harvesting methods. In situations where stones interlock or form a distinct layer, the soil between the stones should be carefully examined to see if roots are able to grow through to the soil below. Stone layers occur commonly in shallow soils over Corallian or other limestones. In many stony soils, it is worthwhile to dig some way into the stones with a crowbar, pick or fork to see if they occur only in a layer, with soil below, or as a fractured upper layer of solid rock.

The pattern of roots can be used directly as an indication of the significance to the crop of any suspect layer in the soil. In a crop growing under unrestricted conditions the root pattern would be related to the species and variety of the crop (Figure 2.1) and to climate; most roots would usually be found in the topsoil with a relatively steady reduction in numbers with depth. Any sharp physical change such as the presence of a pan or smeared layer alters this pattern and where severe panning has occurred a web of roots may be seen on the upper surface of the pan with few or none penetrating. The reaction of roots to compact soil varies with species and variety; the roots of cruciferous and leguminous crops and sugar beet have been found to be particularly sensitive to compact or smeared soil.

Just below the cultivated layer

This zone is one of the most critical so far as crop production is concerned. Below it the soil contains reserves of moisture to sustain crop growth during the season; above it, the soil is loosened regularly by normal cultivations. The most common problem in the zone just below cultivation depth is soil compaction. This is the position of the classical plough-pan. However, it is not only ploughs that may be responsible, the pressure under wheels of tractors and loaded trailers may penetrate to this point.

The signs of excessive compaction are similar to those given above, namely: high density as determined by probing and levering out the soil with a knife or trowel, reduced permeability leading to an accumulation of water or roots above the compact layer (Figure 14.2), a marked discontinuity in structure form often with a horizontal laminated or platy development within the compact layer and possibly a smooth shiny upper surface on the pan, and the absence of pores, fissures, roots or earthworm holes within it. The upper surface may also bear the imprint of cultivator tines or the lugs of tractor tyres, as a direct record of past compression. The thickness of sub-cultivation pans may vary from 1 cm or less to 10 cm or more. It is important to examine this zone carefully and also to look below any suspect layer to see if crop roots have penetrated in significant numbers (Figure 14.4). If the soil has dried to some depth in the subsoil below the pan, this may be a useful indication that roots have been able to penetrate and extract moisture. The boundary at the physical discontinuity between tilled and untilled soil may be mistaken for a soil pan, particularly in late summer when sub-soils may be dry and hard.

The subsoil   The subsoil is normally unaffected by cultivations except deep operations such as subsoiling or field drainage; consequently, this section deals mainly with the identification of natural soil features.

The principal function of the subsoil is to provide entry and egress for percolating water and to permit the entry and extension of crop roots to extract moisture and nutrients. In relatively loose soils roots may be able to push the particles of soil apart as they grow down, but in most they grow through pores (holes within units of structure) and fissures (cracks between units of structure) and to be effective these pathways must be continuous and lead down directly from the porous surface soil above. Pores and fissures may be up to several mm across and can be observed directly by eye, and the presence of roots either living (white) or dead (brown) can be a useful aid. In many soils the wider fissures and pores were probably created many years ago when the land was in forest or marsh when plants with roots much wider than those of present crops were growing (Figures 4.1 and 4.2). Earthworm holes also have a useful function, particularly if they are numerous; they often contain roots and darker coloured top soil, and sometimes follow former root channels.

In some subsoils dominated by sand, root penetration may be very poor, without obvious signs of compaction or hardness. The growth of roots in such soils may extend into the subsoil sand for only 8 – 10 cm and also show a characteristic much-thickened appearance (Figure 4.8).

Loamy soils in their natural state usually provide excellent conditions for root growth, unless affected by acidity or water-logging. Units of structure are often weakly developed but provided roots are readily growing through this is no disadvantage.

In clay soils distinctive and characteristic vertical cracks develop due to shrinkage of the clay particles when they dry. These

FIGURE 14.3 The Significance of Cracks in the Subsoil

Cracks in a clay subsoil filled with dark-coloured peaty topsoil, can act as a pathway for roots and for water draining through the soil.

cracks tend to reform in the same position each year and roots therefore grow also in the same position (Figure 14.2). Horizontal cracks occur too, though these are usually less well developed than those in the vertical plane; and are more common in soils with a moderate clay content and in the upper part of the subsoil.

The major cycle of shrinking and swelling takes place annually and the depth of fracturing is related to the 'dryness' of the climate, that is to the magnitude of the soil water deficit. It is also related to the clay content and to the type of clay present. Within the U K all clay soils contain an adequate proportion of the clays exhibiting shrink-swell cycles.

It is important to realise that these cracks form naturally, deep cultivation is unlikely to produce a beneficial supplement. Indeed if extensive deep cultivation reduces the size of the natural aggregates, it would tend to decrease the width of individual cracks which may lead to slower drainage.

Topsoil often falls down cracks in summer and whether or not this is a beneficial effect is equivocal; chemical fertility may be enhanced but the extra material may give rise to a tighter seal when the clay expands in winter. Because roots can be so readily seen on crack faces in the subsoil, their presence is a good guide to the absence of any limiting feature higher up the soil profile.

Cemented and indurated layers

As well as man-made barriers, naturally occurring hard layers can be found, which may severely affect crops and land capability. In the Midlands of England and in East Anglia cemented gravels and sands may occur, usually associated with a high water table. These may be very hard and, if shallow, may require to be broken by heavy cultivators or even by explosives before they can be removed from the land. In Northern Britain indurrated layers occur in many sandy and loamy soils within 30 − 50 cm of the surface; these are relics of the Ice Age (Figure 2.3). Their presence is rarely in doubt as they are extremely hard, a strong blow with a spade may penetrate less than 1 cm. Their direct significance for crop growth is less than expected because of the cooler wetter climate in which they occur; the main hazard is to drainage.

FIGURE 14.4 Compaction and Root Growth
A dense subsoil restricting the development of sugar beet roots in late summer.

Numerical Evaluation of Soil Conditions The objective in the previous sections of this chapter, was to give guidance on the use of soil examination as a key technique in the care of the soil, mainly by visual assessment of the physical condition, and to identify features both good and poor, in relation to the management of the soil. However, there are several situations where it can be an advantage to classify the physical state of the soil into a number of specific categories. For example in an experiment where different treatments have created a range of soil conditions, or where regular monitoring of field structure is required. These type of tests, sometimes termed visual scores, can be further modified to improve their sensitivity to match the range of conditions found on a particular site, or alternatively a new test can be devised. The only requirements are that each condition allocated to a class or number should be defined, and that there should be some logical progression along the scale. Visual scoring of soil conditions also encourages the detailed examination of key features. The flexibility of such tests also provides a means of recording any variation in soil structure, where verbal descriptions would not only be tedious to do, but almost impossible to compare. It is also possible to submit numerical values for statistical analysis and interpretion.

As examples of visual scores, two methods are described, one for the direct evaluation of soil structure in the field, and the other for assessing the softness of the soil surface (squelch test).

1. Field Assessment of Soil Structure

The objective of this method is to examine and assess the quality of soil structure in a layer of soil by assigning to it a numerical value. The evaluation is designed primarily for the assessment of the tilled layer and of the soil just beneath it. This type of descriptive test was first developed in The Netherlands by P.K. Peerlkamp and P. Boekel.

The advantages of the test described below, and others like it, include:

● it is a field test, no samples need to be collected and taken for laboratory investigations; the soil is quickly and systematically assessed and recorded on the spot.

● changes as a result of a single cultivation can be assessed.

● it has value as a diagnostic assessment for comparisons between poor and good areas.

● it can be used on experiments where variation in soil condition has been induced and requires evaluation.

● it can be used to record short term or long term changes and the effects of management and weather on the soil condition.

Method

An area of soil or crop should be selected which shows features typical of the land to be examined. Begin at the surface and dig out a spadeful of soil, gently break this apart by hand and assess the size and condition of the aggregates if they are loose; if the layer is hard and comes away as a complete block, assess its strength and continuity. Use the key below to assign a number to the soil as a whole. Then clear away enough of the upper soil to enable a second spadeful to be extracted and examined in the same way. If any change in soil condition occurs within the depth of a spadeful, assess each layer separately. Measure the depth of each layer, normally only two. If any layer has a distinct smeared and shining appearance on the upper surface, note this condition and whether the smear is continuous or only partly covering the surface.

SOIL STRUCTURE KEY

i) for loose soil:

> a layer consisting of separate lumps of soil, some of the larger ones may be broken further by gentle hand pressure. Four groups are distinguished, based on the size of the lumps:

S1 Fine aggregates, 1 − 6 mm in diameter

S2 Predominantly medium sized aggregates, mainly 6 − 10 mm in diamter, some smaller, and possibly an occasional lump up to 20 mm across.

S3 Coarse aggregates, mainly 10 − 30 mm in diameter with an occasional lump up to 50 mm.

S4 Very coarse aggregates, mainly 30 − 70 mm in diameter.

A combined assessment may also be used, such as S2 + S3, 50/50.

ii) for a firm layer of soil:

S5 Soil weakly but distinctly combined into a layer which may be partially or wholly complete, can be broken readily by hand into individual aggregates − these may in turn be assessed as in S1 to S4 above to give combined assessment of S5.1, S5.2, S5.3 or S5.4.

S6 Soil strongly combined into a layer which can be broken up only with distinct force by hand − the subunits may be assessed to give a combined assessment of S6.1, S6.2, S6.3, and S6.4.

S7 A compact layer, with few or no component aggregates visible, broken with difficulty into angular sub-units. Further classification based on size is not feasible as the size obtained by breaking depends on the force applied. If anaerobic conditions are detected within the layer, the designation S7.0 may be given.

2. Surface Squelch Test

Where variation in the softness and wetness of the surface is of interest, a numerical scale of squelchiness can be used. This type of test was first used by the M.A.F.F. Field Drainage Experimental Unit, but the method described below deals only with softness and excludes categories for frost and snow, used in the original version. As stated earlier, visual scores of this type are meant to be flexible, and can be further modified to meet the needs of a specific range of conditions encountered.

SQ 1 Surface firm, no compression by foot pressure

SQ 2 Surface loose, penetration by foot pressure of up to 2 cm

SQ 3 Surface slightly soft to foot pressure, penetration up to 5 cm

SQ 4 Surface distinctly soft, foot penetration greater than 5 cm

SQ 5 Very soft and wet, water on surface, foot imprint deeper than 7 − 10 cm

SQ 6 Water standing on a firm surface

Chapter 15   GOOD SOIL HUSBANDRY

At the outset the intention was that this book should be of interest primarily to those who both use and care for the soil. It is hoped that by reading it those managers and users have gained some insight into what I consider to be the six principal tenets of good soil husbandry. These are:

1. Crop rotations: the choice of crops and how they are grown and harvested must match the quality and limitations of the land. Examples were given in Chapter 12.

2. Soil Organic Matter: this is a key asset influencing soil structure and crop nutrition and as such, its value should not be ignored. It is important to recognize the signs associated with the approach of critical levels, as discussed in Chapter 5.

3. Field Drainage: sound drainage is an important requirement for many soils and requires a system to be correctly designed and installed, followed by regular clearing of drains and maintenance of visible outfalls. Chapters 7 and 10 discuss this topic.

4. Attention to Soil Structure: on the surface, the reaction of bare soil to the impact of heavy rain is a good guide to the stability of structure; under wheeltracks and tramlines reduced permeability may lead to erosion and to the formation of wet patches. It is important to understand how these conditions arise and to take appropriate action, discussed in Chapters 4, 8, 9 and 14.

5. Cultivations: the choice and timing of cultivation should plan to avoid unnecessary compaction; any damage caused inadvertantly must be dealt with after examining the soil. Decisions on the need for subsoiling and how it should be done must also be based on examination of the soil and not on blind faith that it might do some good. These points were amplified in Chapter 8.

6. Dig and look: regular examination of soils should be establ-, ished as a routine, in good seasons as well as in bad. This point is discussed in almost every chapter.

There is therefore much that users can do themselves but professional advice is always available for those lacking exper- ience or for the more tricky situations.

Despite the emphasis on soil problems in this book, there is no doubt that in the temperate climate of Britain, much of our land is in good heart and does all that is asked of it year in and year out. However, farming does not remain unchanged but responds to political and economic forces, and to technical advances — grants and quotas, fewer staff, larger tractors, new chemicals. Farmers are thus concerned not only with knowledge of the present state of their land, but in knowing what long-term effects any of their current practices are having on the soil, and how it will respond to new technology or crops. Apart from safeguard- ing 'mankind's greatest natural resource', if the principles of good soil husbandry are followed, they also make good econo- mic sense in our present climate of changing land use. This is because soil examination and evaluation may reduce losses res- ulting from erosion and compaction, obviate the need for subsoi- ling and hopefully maintain or increase yields and quality. Soil problems are many, varied and idiosyncratic, and no attempt has been made to cover every eventuality or the wide choice of cultivation implements or methods. Nevertheless, the general principles of soil husbandry stand, in whatever circumstances and in whatever context soil problems occur.

APPENDIX

1. LIST OF COMPLEMENTARY BOOKS

The following books are recommended where readers wish to have more information on specific topics, and should be regarded as complementary to SOIL HUSBANDRY.

1. General Introductory Books

AN INTRODUCTION TO SOIL SCIENCE. E.A. Fitzpatrick. 1986. Second Edition
    Longman.

SOIL. K. Simpson. 1983. Longman.

INTRODUCTION TO THE PRINCIPLES AND PRACTICE OF SOIL SCIENCE. R.E. White.
    1987. Second Edition. Blackwell.

MODERN FARMING AND THE SOIL. Ministry of Agriculture, Fisheries and Food.
    1970. H.M.S.O. London.

2. Books and reports giving more detailed accounts on specialised topics.

RUSSELL'S SOIL CONDITIONS AND PLANT GROWTH. Edited by A. Wild
    Eleventh Edition 1988. Longman.

SOIL RESOURCES SURVEYS, INTERPRETATIONS AND APPLICATIONS. E.J.B. Cutler.
    1977. Lincoln College Press, Canterbury, New Zealand.

SOIL SURVEY AND LAND EVALUATION. D. Dent and A. Young. 1981. George
    Allen and Unwin.

PLANT ROOT SYSTEMS. R.S. Russell. 1977. McGraw-Hill.

M.A.F.F. TECHNICAL BULLETINS:
          No. 13 SOIL PHOSPHORUS 1965
          No. 14 SOIL POTASSIUM AND MAGNESIUM 1967
          No. 21 TRACE ELEMENTS IN SOILS & CROPS 1971

APPENDIX

No. 29 SOIL PHYSICAL CONDITIONS AND CROP
PRODUCTION 1975
All from H.M.S.O. London

FERTILISERS AND MANURES. K. Simpson. 1986. Longman.

SOIL MANAGEMENT. D.B. Davies, D.J. Eagle and J.B. Finney. 1982 4th
Edition. Farming Press.

FERTILISER RECOMMENDATIONS.
i. Scottish Agricultural Colleges 1985.
Publication No. 160.
ii. M.A.F.F. Reference Book 209 1983.

LAND DRAINAGE. E. Farr & W.C. Henderson. 1987. Longman.

LAND DRAINAGE: planning and design of agricultural drainage systems.
L.K.Smedema & D.W. Rycroft. 1983. Batsford.

ALTERNATIVE ENTERPRISES FOR AGRICULTURE IN THE U K. Ed.
S.P. Carruthers.
1986. Report 11 Centre for Agricultural Strategy. Univ. of Reading.

OVER-COMPACTION OF SOILS ON SCOTTISH FARMS: A SURVEY.
B.D. Soane. 1987.
Scottish Inst. of Agric. Engineering.

PERMANENT GRASSLAND STUDIES 2. Grassland Poaching in England
and Wales
(with provisional map) P.M. Patto, C.R. Clement & T.J. Forbes. 1978.
A.G.R.I. Hurley, Maidenhead, Berkshire.

WATER, SOIL AND THE PLANT. E.J. Winter. 1974. MacMillan.

ADVISORY LEAFLETS AND BOOKLETS:
There are numerous well written publications dealing with soil related topics
available from ADAS, and the Scottish Colleges. For example on subsoiling,
drainage, liming, trace elements and cultivations. To obtain a list of current
titles from ADAS, write to:
MAFF (Publications), Lion House,
Willowburn Estate, Alnwick,
Northumberland NE 66 2 PF

For Scottish Agricultural Colleges publications write to Area Offices or to The
Librarian, at one of the three Colleges.

3. Publications of the Soil Survey of Great Britain.

A list of these can be obtained from the Survey Headquarters:

England & Wales: Silsoe Campus, Silsoe, Bedford NK 45 6DT
Scotland: Macaulay Land Use Research Institute,
      Craigiebuckler, Aberdeen AB2 4DL.

2. METRIC (SI) UNITS AND CONVERSIONS TO OTHER UNITS

Length

1 millimetre (mm) — 0.0394 inch
1 centimetre (cm) = 0.394 inch
1 metre (m) = 1.094 yard
     = 3.28 feet
1 kilometre (km) — 0.621 mile — 1094 yards

Area

1 hectare (ha) = 2.47 acres

Mass

1 tonne (t) = 2205 pounds
    = 0.984 ton
1 kilogram (kg) = 2.205 pounds

Rates of Application

1 kg/ha = 0.89 lb/ac
1 t/ha = 0.40 ton/ac

Other useful figures:

1 mm rain is approximately 10 t/ha

1 hectare average mineral soil to a depth of 15 cm (6 ins.) has a mass of approximately 2500 tonne (1000 ton/acre)

3. GLOSSARY

Anaerobic conditions: literally without air, but in soils is usually taken to mean without oxygen, a state which can occur when soils are waterlogged and/or compacted. When soil oxygen is exhausted and unavailable to meet the respiratory needs of aerobic organisms in the soil, those tolerant of anaerobic conditions take over which can decompose nitrate to gaseous forms of nitrogen and produce toxic gases such as hydrogen sulphide and ethylene.

Available Water: that proportion of water retained by a soil that can be absorbed by plant roots, usually defined as the water held in soil between field capacity and permanent wilting point.

Field Capacity: the water retained by a soil just after any excess has drained out under the influence of gravity.

Denitrification: the conversion of nitrate to nitrogen gas or to other gases such as nitrous oxide which are unavailable to plants and lost from the soil.

APPENDIX

Humus: the relatively stable fraction of organic matter remaining after the decomposition of any plant residues and animal manures added to the soil.

Leaching: removal of nutrients in solution from the soil by the downward passage of water.

Mole drain: an unlined underground smooth-walled channel formed by pulling a bullet-shaped device through the soil.

Ochre, or iron ochre: an orange or reddish brown rust-coloured sediment, sometimes filamentous, found in or around field drain pipes which forms when soluble iron compounds encounter oxygen in the open drain and are converted to insoluble forms. Microbial organisms are sometimes involved.

Permanent Wilting Point: the water retained by soil when plants growing in it wilt and do not recover. This is commonly done by squeezing water out of soil by a pressure of 15 bar.

Permeable back-fill, or porous back-fill: graded gravel or other material placed in the trench above a drain pipe to act as a highly permeable link between the pipe and any mole or subsoiler channel cut across

Poaching: compression or displacement of the soil surface caused by the pressure of animal hooves applied to soft soils.

Pore Space: the voids between the soil particles which are normally occupied by air and/or water.

Soil capping or surface crusting: the disintegration, reorientation and packing of soil particles on the surface as a result of heavy rain falling on bare soil or when a soil is flooded.

Soil pan: a layer of soil that has been significantly compacted by the application of pressure.

Soil structure: the arrangement of individual soil particles into porous aggregates, together with the pore space within and between the aggregates.

Soil texture: the physical composition of the soil as determined by the sizes and proportion of the individual particles of sand, silt and clay present

Soil water deficit: the dryness of the soil usually in terms of the quantity of water (mm) required to return the soil to field capacity.

Subsoiling: a tillage operation designed to loosen soil beneath the normal depth of ploughing or cultivation.

Weathering: the reduction in size, alteration or decomposition of rocks by physical, chemical and biological action.

INDEX

As this book was written as a practical guide rather than a scientific textbook, the index has been prepared to help readers find information related to specific problems that may be encountered in a field situation.